"So widely famed was the Bishop as a traveller, and so great his reputation as a connoisseur of all good things, that Lord Bristol's Hotel – he was latterly known everywhere on the Continent as Lord Bristol – came to be the best known and regarded in every city or town where he sojourned and was thus the precursor of the Hotels Bristol to be found all over Europe."

— *William Shakespeare Childe-Pemberton,*
author of 'The Earl Bishop', 1924

"Many hotels around the world claim that they were allowed to name their house after Frederick Augustus Hervey, the 4th Earl of Bristol. This is of course nonsense since the majority of these hotels opened their doors over 100 years after the Earl died. Furthermore, these hotels also carry the coat of arms of Bristol, a city, not an aristocrat."

— *Andreas Augustin,*
President, The Most Famous Hotels in the World

High Times
at the
Hotel Bristol

Twenty bedside tales

Roger Williams

First published 2007
by Roger Williams © All rights reserved
bristolbook@btinternet.com

Cover design and typesetting by Roger Williams
Typeset in Adobe Garamond 11/13pt & Gill Sans

Printed and bound in Great Britain
by Cox & Wyman, Reading, Berkshire

ISBN 978-0-9555376-0-8

A romantic weekend at Le Bristol hotel in Paris marks the beginning of the end for international financial adviser Tom Cotton. As he begins to uncover the secrets of just some of the scores of hotels around the world named after the scandalous 4th Earl of Bristol, his own life becomes inextricably mixed with theirs.
The result is an intriguing collection of bedside stories based on the adventures of Tom Cotton and on real events in the life of Lord Bristol and the hotels that bear his name.

Roger Williams' novels include *Lunch with Elizabeth David,* *Burning Barcelona, A-Train* and *Aftermath.* Non-fiction includes *The Royal Albert Hall: a Masterpiece for the 21st Century* and many travel guides

CONTENTS

1: WHAT'S IN A NAME?

The Ickworth Hotel
Horringer, Suffolk, England
www.ickworthhotel.com

Why on earth call a hotel Bristol? This question cropped up nearly twenty years ago when Sophie and I spent a few days away for the first time shortly after we had met. I still look back on that weekend at Le Bristol in Paris with fondness, in spite of the painful break-up a dozen years later. Sophie was French Swiss, bright, brown-eyed, efficient and kind, and to cement our romance we had chosen to spend a weekend in one of the most elegant and historic hotels in the city. Over breakfast on the first morning, as I reached out to dust a croissant crumb from her lower lip, I wondered aloud why such a sophisticated establishment as Le Bristol would want to call itself after a small and not very glamorous English port. In the endearing lilt that had attracted me from the start, Sophie replied that if it had been called Le Bog*nor* or Le Basing*stoke,* we would probably have gone elsewhere. I am sure she was right.

Sophie worked for an international public relations company and I was employed by an international finance house specialising in European Union tax laws, living on expense accounts and out of suitcases. We were on the way up our heady career ladders. After our Parisian break, I started to notice other hotels called Bristol and at every opportunity I checked them out. They spread beyond Europe, from Amman to Buenos Aires, Delhi to San Diego, Yalta to Melbourne, and ideas about how this might have come about started to emerge, too.

One of the most popular theories is that they are named after Frederick Augustus Hervey (pronounced Harvey, 1730–1803), the 4th Earl Bristol, who became Bishop of Derry, Ireland's richest episcopal see. He was a worldly cleric from a family of scarlet women and outspoken and eccentric men of whom it was said, "There are men, women and Herveys". A larger than life character, he embraced materialism and used his well paid position to dash about Europe collecting paintings and antiquities to fill the mansions he was building for himself. These were Downhill and Ballyscullion in Derry, neither of which survives, and Ickworth in Suffolk, which he built after inheriting the estate and lodge, along with his title, from his older brother at the age of forty-four. The Earl-Bishop spent little time in Derry and hardly any time in Suffolk but he managed to build and furnish these sumptuous homes. In his own parish he is remembered for putting spires on churches, building roads, draining bogs and supporting the Volunteers. In Suffolk, the house he built is on the tourist map.

Centred on a grand neo-classical rotunda designed to exhibit the continual consigments of art that Bristol dispatched from Europe, Ickworth today is a major attraction. Handsomely furnished, it has a number of family portraits, including several of the Earl-Bishop. One by Hugh Douglas Hamilton, painted when Bristol was sixty, shows a fresh-faced cleric with a high forehead and pale hair reaching the collar of his black tunic of office. He is seated in a fashionably romantic arbour overlooking the city of Rome. The house and gardens are run by the National Trust, to whom it was given by the 6th Marquess of Bristol in 1956. Part of it was opened as a 27-bedroom hotel in 2002, three years after the death of the 7th Marquess who had squandered much of what remained of the family fortune on drugs. The title subsequently passed to twenty-year-old Frederick William Augustus Hervey, who was studying architecture at Edinburgh University. Lady Victoria and Lady Isabelle Hervey, "It" Girl and Playboy bunny, are the 8th Marquess's sisters.

The Earl-Bishop spent a total of twenty years on the Continent, including the last eleven of his life. Restless, and found, though it was suggested that many Polish names may be unpronounceable to foreign visitors. Michael Goerdt, who was general manager of the same Warsaw Bristol when it reopened after a major refurbishment in 1993, believes that the name Bristol became widespread simply because, like Astoria, it is a word that can be pronounced in any language, and is easy on the tongue even when transliterated into Cyrillic.

Going further, Andreas Augustin, author of handsome hotel books and president of The Most Famous Hotels in the World, refutes the Earl-Bishop theory entirely, insisting this was simply a "bad PR gag". It is the English city of Bristol, he maintains, that gives the hotels their names, pointing to the Vienna Bristol's logo bearing the English city's coat of arms. When the Bristol in Rome opened in 1870, it, too employed this coat of arms, and he believes that this was the first hotel in the world to be named Bristol.

In the northern Greek city of Thessaloniki, the Capsis family, who have been running the Bristol since it opened in 1917, agree. The English port, they say, is "where the concept of modern hotels was born when, for the first time, an inn separated customers from their horses and created rooms for customers and special spaces for horses". The Capsis go on to say that tradition insists that every town is allowed to host only one Bristol, though I have found this is not always the case.

The West Country maritime city is not an obvious candidate for such fame. The slave trade that helped it to prosper is nothing to crow about, and though it achieved acclaim when John Cabot set out from there in 1497 to explore North America, where more than thirty towns took Bristol's name, it is far less glamorous than, say, Marseilles or Barcelona. And yet, one way and another, the name has spread.

In the twentieth century the name of Bristol was romanticised and scattered to the four winds by the city's aviation company. Its famous Boxkite carried the first airmail letters in Britain and took them around the world. Bristol Aviation built cargo carriers and fighter planes that became household names in both World Wars and its Britannia airlines took passengers on transatlantic and colonial routes in the 1950s. Concorde became airborne with its participation. The Bristol company made road vehicles, too, and although the commercial vehicle manufacturers was subsumed into British Leyland in the 1970s, you can still see the Bristol logo on buses in South Africa and on open-top tourist buses crossing New York's Times Square.

Bristol Cars Ltd is the last remaining British luxury car maker and their hand-make sports cars are among the most expensive in the world.

There may be more mundane reasons for choosing the name Bristol. The handsome clapboard Hotel Bristol in downtown Steamboat Springs, Colorado, for instance, takes its name from Police Chief Everett Bristol, who built the place in 1948. Occasionally, the name goes out of fashion, especially in moments of anti-British feeling, such as the 20th century's World Wars when all Bristols disappeared in Germany. But by and large the name has endured remarkably well, adapting to the markets of its times. True, many of them have been lost, but hotels continue to open under the tried-and-tested Bristol name.

Every hotel has a score of stories. And as I booked in and out of a succession of hotels Bristol, collecting souvenir labels, pens, toiletries, towels and dressing gowns that filled our bathroom and drove Sophie crazy, my own life became a part of theirs. In the end I decided to set down these tales, anecdotes and histories in a book, with each hotel providing a chapter, a complete episode that would take no longer to read than you would want in the time from falling into bed and getting settled before switching out the light. It would be the ideal bedside reader for any hotel, no matter what its name.

Tom Cotton
The Ideal Hotel Bristol
The Maghreb

2: FREUD'S ENEMA

Bristol Palace Hotel
Karlovy Vary (Karlsbad), Czech Republic
www. bristol.cz

The first time Lord Bristol visited the Continent was in 1765. He was Frederick Hervey then, aged thirty-four and living in the Suffolk village of Horringer beside the Ickworth estate of his older brother, the 3rd Earl of Bristol. He and his wife Elizabeth Davers planned a year abroad, visiting Voltaire, an old family friend, at Fernay near Geneva, and William Hamilton, who had shared many interests with him since their schooldays at Westminster and who was now British Minister to the King of the Two Sicilies in Naples.

The Herveys took their children with them. Eleven-year-old Mary was the oldest (she later married the Earl of Erne), then came George, aged nine, and Elizabeth, the future Duchess of Devonshire. Their youngest son John, called Jack by the family, seems to have been left at home for his education. Mary and Elizabeth were to remain in Geneva for the year with a governess, Mademoiselle Chaumel, to learn French, the language of the court of George III, to whom Hervey was now Chaplain.

On landing on the Continent, the family entourage headed for the Belgian town of Spa, famous for its therapeutic waters. Portraits of Frederick Hervey from around this time, by Battoni and Zofany, show a slim man with a long and shining, clean-shaven face. His light hair, combed flat with a centre parting, drops straight down to end in a few curls around his ears, a hairstyle that echoes the periwig he would wear on formal occasions. Despite these pictures of health, throughout his life the Earl-Bishop suffered bouts of infirmity particularly from gout, which he claimed was hereditary, though the fact that he was able to drink a bottle of Madeira "like a gentleman" undoubtedly compounded the ailment. Like many people of his era, he believed in the curative properties of natural mineral waters, of which he became a connoisseur. He had visited Bath and Bristol Wells, and he was yet to discover his favourite spa at Pyrmont in Germany, where he would buy a house and build roads for the benefit of its most illustrious visitor, King Frederick of Prussia.

On that first visit to Spa, however, tragedy struck. George, their oldest boy, died, presumably from some malady that the family was hoping the therapeutic waters would cure. Frederick William, their seventh and last surviving child, born four years afterwards, later returned to Spa to look for the grave of his oldest brother. But Protestants in the Catholic Ardennes were not accorded official burials, and he could find no trace of it. (Frederick outlived his older brother Jack to become 5th Earl and 1st Marquess of Bristol; the Herveys also had another girl, Louise, who married the future Prime Minister, Lord Liverpool.)

I had never imagined I would ever seek the benefits offered by a spa, particularly the Continental type, those monolithic institutions that seem just a few crawling steps away from the grave. But in the spring of 1995 a series of events led me to the spa town of Karlsbad in the Czech Republic, a new country that was emerging from half a century of communism. The Velvet Revolution had been won, Prague had replaced Paris as the place where aspiring American writers most wanted to live to start their literary careers, and many people were trying to connect with Eastern Europe. Sophie's mother was one of them.

Just before Easter she called from Geneva, inviting Sophie to join her for a fortnight at the Bristol Palace, one of Karlsbad's grand retreats. At first Sophie was reluctant to go. In spite of her Swiss upbringing, she felt the same way as I did about old-fashioned spas, but it was unlike Fernande to issue such an invitation and Sophie did not want to let her down.

"I feel that Mamma wants to talk," Sophie said as she related the conversation over a mid-week meal in a Korean restaurant we had recently discovered in St Giles High Street, "but I don't know about what."

"Do you think it's about Patrice?" I asked. "Perhaps he's having an affair."

She laughed. "Pappa? You are joking."

Patrice was a corporate lawyer and the couple lived a spotless bourgeois life in their villa beside Lake Geneva with no more help than a live-in maid and a twice-weekly gardener. A trim and habitually busy woman, Fernande worked for the World Health Organisation and was a walking advertisement for natural well being. Like anyone from the nation of big pharmaceutical companies, both she and her daughter were strangers to indulgence, and whenever they were sick they never hesitated in reaching for a pill or medicine bottle, which was guaranteed to work.

"Colonic irrigation," Sophie said. "I bet that's what people have at the Bristol. Can you think of anything more disgusting?"

I tried to reassure her, saying that treatment would not be compulsory and if the hotel was anything like Le Bristol in Paris, she should be well looked after. She needed a break. Work at her PR agency had been tough. Through no fault of her own she had just lost a major client, and she was pushing herself hard to find new business to make up for it. As a result she was loath to be away from her desk for long. In the end she agreed to go for just four days, flying to Geneva and driving with her mother to Karlsbad, then flying back to London from Prague.

When I telephoned on her first night, she confirmed our worst fears. True, the Bristol was a fairytale Viennese-style château in a picturesque river valley, but it had become an East European dump. It was April. Wind was ripping young leaves from the Bohemian trees, and the rain would not stop. But for a dip in the pool and a massage, Sophie had been curled up for most of the day with Voltaire's *Candide*, watching water dribble under an ill-fitting balcony door while her mother had begun a course of treatment designed to relieve stress.

"She isn't really stressed, Tom," Sophie assured me. "But she couldn't think of any other complaint that needed treatment. The doctor wanted me to try some balneotherapy, too – or electrotherapy or magnetotherapy or gas inhalations. Can you imagine? They all sound like torture. I still smell of chlorine from the swimming pool, *perrf!* And the woman who gave me a massage... *eeerh!* The thermal water tastes horrible, *yeagh!* I don't know how people drink so much of it. They tell me I must give up alcohol and caffeine, but it makes me want to drink. Besides I'm a paying guest, *I* will tell *them* what I should do."

Apart from a few skinny Slavic girls who were with Russian mafia men, she said, everyone was old and ugly. And the food was terrible – "We had dumplings and stewed fruit for dinner. Have you eaten tonight?"

"I'm just going down to the Royal China in Westferry Circus."

"God, don't tell me. I wish I could come."

"I wish you could, too."

I was happy enough eating in restaurants alone, catching up on news magazines and papers in sociable surroundings. But I felt sorry for Sophie. It wasn't often that she complained, and I knew she would be anxious to be back at work. The second time we spoke, she was even lower. She had finished *Candide* and had been disappointed to find no reading material whatsoever provided by the hotel. A tour of the town had revealed little hope of any other diversion.

"The shops are naked," she said. "The economy is broken. The whole country is empty. It's just so much of nothing."

I told her not to worry; she would soon be home. The next night there was no reply from her hotel room but the following day she rang me at work just before lunch. I had been at our Canada Water office for more than two solid weeks, which was a long stretch in those travelling days. She sounded excited.

"I'm sorry I missed you last night," she said. "Mamma and I were... I don't know quite what.... She's found this Russian. It's probably nothing."

I probed. Alexei Machinek was a Muscovite. Mid-forties, businessman, wads of cash, a fake tan. It did not sound good.

"She's talking about investing in the spa."

"Blimey."

"Machinek wants her to put money into the Bristol."

"Does he own it?"

"Not yet. They're privatising it under the new voucher system and there is an opportunity to invest."

"The voucher system is meant to stop foreigners taking over."

"He is confident he can do it."

"What does your father say?"

"Mamma has told me not to talk to him about it."

This was serious. Fernande was not an impetuous woman, nor, as far as I knew, was she in the habit of asking her daughter to side against Patrice.

"So," Sophie said. "What do you think?"

"I think I'll stay on for a few more days."

That evening I lingered over dinner. Although I did not mind eating alone, I was less content living alone. So much of my time was spent travelling that our high-rent Docklands flat often seemed alien to me, and now I found myself becoming reluctant to return to it at the end of the day. It had the depressing ability to look exactly the same in the evening as it had when I left it in the morning. The cleaner came only once a week, there was never anything in the fridge, nowhere to leave my shirts to be laundered, and as yet no cable television to watch world-wide news. Before the restaurant bill came, I had decided to fly out to the Czech Republic just as soon as I could.

The first available flight was on Sunday morning. On Saturday afternoon I went over to Hackney to visit my brother James and his wife Kate. A few years older than me, James worked for a charity that operated in developing countries and he was then involved with the Maya people in Central America. He was away nearly as often as I was, abandoning Kate, a remedial teacher, and their two children, who now went to school and were too old to tag along on his adventures. Perhaps because we didn't see too much of each other, we got on well. We often compared travelling notes, discussing airlines, cities, countries, and the best and worst places to eat and sleep. That afternoon we took the two boys and a football to the park and as we were kicking around I mentioned Sophie's mother's new ambitions in the hospitality industry.

"The Bristol Palace in Karlsbad...well, well." He knew of my incipient interest in the Earl-Bishop of Ickworth. "I was reading about it only the other day in Eddie Bernays' obituary."

"Eddie who?"

"I meant to tear it out and keep it for you. It's probably been thrown away by now."

"Thanks a bunch." I snatched the ball from him. Though four years older than me, James was fitter, and he could still run rings around the boys. We chased about till I was puffed, then we left it to the boys and sat on a bench.

"Edward J. Bernays was the inventor of public relations," James said, keeping his eye on the kids, "a wizard of the dark arts, the Father of Spin. He was the maestro of manipulating public opinion and he died last month at the ripe old age of 103."

I was none the wiser. The ball came scooting towards us and we both made a grab for it. James won. "You're unfit, Tom," he said, "even if you don't ever put on any weight."

"I'm fit for what I do. My job involves a lot of sitting down. If I was any fitter, I'd only get restless and want to wander about."

"You need children to keep you fit." He kicked the ball high in the air and the kids ran to be first underneath it.

"Nobody needs children. They're all horrible." I never liked James telling me how I should lead my life.

"So why are you always so nice to my two?"

In their attempts to reach the ball first, the boys clashed and fell into a cursing heap on the grass.

"I feel sorry for them having to live with you."

"Ha ha."

"Tell me about this Bernays."

Tom shouted at the boys to stop their spat otherwise he would take them home. When play resumed, he said, "An American whizz-kid who got presidents elected, made it socially acceptable for women to smoke, invented the American egg-and-bacon breakfast, wrote a book called *Propaganda*, which Joseph Goebels, the Nazis' Minister of Propaganda, kept prominently on his bookshelf, and in the 1950s he single-handedly orchestrated opinion sufficiently to convince the American government to overthrow the democratically elected government in Guatemala so that his clients, the United Fruit Company, could keep making large profits. It left Latin America in the grip of US-backed dictators for decades.

"Hence your interest…"

"Civil war in Guatemala is still going on."

"And what has all that got to do with the Bristol in Karlsbad?"

"According to the obituary, when he was a young man just before the First World War, Bernays went there to meet his favourite uncle, Sigmund Freud. He was just starting out and Uncle Sigi helped him formulate his ideas for mass manipulation of public minds, what he called 'engineering of consent'."

"What was Freud doing at the Bristol?"

"He had migraines."

"Did it cure him?"

"I have no idea. *Yours!*" The ball suddenly came hurtling towards us at head height and I ducked to avoid being smattered with mud. James called me a chicken, then went on, "But I would have loved to have overheard the conversations between the Father of Psychoanalysis and his protégé, the Father of Spin."

The next day, Sunday, I rose early and caught a plane to Prague where I hired a car to drive the sixty kilometres to Karlovy Vary, the Czech name for Karlsbad. I had been to Prague a number of times over the previous couple of years. The collapse of communism had given my employers limitless opportunities and the Russian I had studied along with economics at university was suddenly a great asset. In the first half of the 1990s my feet barely touched the ground. In fact I was away from the London office more often than not. Our business was to facilitate Western businessmen in the new markets, and help aspirant nations deal with the bureaucracy international funding bodies and institutions, particularly the EU. When I joined the company at the end of 1989 there we re a dozen employees. By now there we re six times as many and we had opened offices in Paris, Berlin and Budapest. But this was the first time I had driven in the Czech countryside, and I could see what Sophie meant. There we re few cars on the pock-marked road and little sign of life in the towns. It did look empty, and it was hard to imagine tourists flocking here. The idea of investing in a provincial hotel was simply a non-starter.

It was just getting dark when I arrived, and the town at first seemed rather grand. It had a sort of fairytale aspect that the sulphurous street lights encouraged, with vast hotel mansions and long colonnades by the river where the spring waters were drunk. It wasn't hard to imagine it as a place favoured by Bach and Beethoven, Schiller and Goethe, though the few people now out in the streets, in jeans and cheap trainers, were all nobodies. Less than. Scaffolding enfolded a couple of buildings, and as I got closer I saw the crumbling balconies and neglected facades, and realised it wasn't just the sulphurous lighting that gave the buildings a rich patina. There was an industrial brown film over the whole town. Even the Pupp was under wraps. Pupp was the grandest of the spa hotels but in communist days it changed its name to the Moskva when the Russians had a monopoly over it, sending their welfare cases here. At first I thought it was closed, but as I approached I saw lights we re on behind the scaffolding and tarpaulins. Somebody came out and climbed into a limousine parked right outside. It was Václav Havel. I had once been in the same room as the Czech president, but we had never spoken. Stooped and grey, he looked a typical spa guest, and in fact it was only a few months later that he was diagnosed as having lung cancer.

The Bristol Palace was the most glamorous building in the Bristol hotel complex of five separate hotel buildings at the west end of town on top of Castle Hill. The buildings, mostly former private villas, were flaking and jaundiced. I parked the car and went into the lobby. I expected to step back into the Edwardian era. Instead, the furnishings and fittings, the bare bulbs and functional tables and chairs, were more like the 1950s, and it smelt that old, too.

Sophie and I had agreed the plan: I was to tell Fernande that I had work to do in Prague – not too much of a lie, because there was some business I could cover while I was there – and that I would be staying for a few nights at the Bristol, commuting daily to the capital.

She appeared in the lobby in slacks and a large sweater and her chestnut hair looked dull and ragged. She had not bothered with make-up. The hostile surroundings made her seem vulnerable, almost childish, and if I was pleased to see her, she was relieved to see me.

"Good trip?" Her habitual two-cheek kiss was delivered with less than its usual perfunctory speed.

"Just fine." I took her hand.

She led me up a clanking elevator and along thread-bare carpets in corridors that smelt of damp and cheap tobacco. Our room was plain, the bed concave and the pillows foam. There was no television, mini-bar or safe, and of course no plug in the sink. As I hung up my shirts and washed, Sophie filled me in on the Fernande situation, though there wasn't much to tell, except that her mother seemed to have become enamoured of this Russian businessman.

"I don't dislike him," she said. "But I don't trust him."

"Do you think your mother is contemplating an affair?"

"I don't think so, but I'm really not sure what's going on." She waved her arms to encompass the surroundings. "She is talking about putting a lot of money into this...this *latrine*."

Fernande joined us for dinner in the hotel restaurant, where there was only a smattering of diners. Even in her mid-fifties there was something gamine about her, with her short, unfussed hair and the minimum of make-up, and clothes that were always simply stylish. The depressing surroundings may have got to Sophie, but Fernande glowed.

"There is nowhere else worth eating in town," Sophie said as we settled into our corner table. "Don't think I haven't checked. And don't have the wine here, have beer. The wine is disgusting." She didn't mind that the waiter heard. He didn't look as if he cared either; he would be one of many workers who would sell his vouchers to the highest bidder.

The matter of the Russian and the investment was delicate; it was not for me to bring it up, but over roast pork with dumplings and cabbage, Fernande began to extoll the virtues of the Bristol and outlined her vision of spas being the hotels of the future. She saw beyond the *kurhaus* to the pharmaceutical and cosmetics industries that were embarked on serious campaigns to convince the public that they deserved pampering, grooming, and physically improving. She made spas with a scalpel sound cutting edge.

"Sophie is cynical about the balneotherapy, Tom," she said. "But as a businessman you must see that what some people will pay to look and feel nice cannot be underestimated. And these new cheap flights will make weekend breaks possible and turn not just cities, but individual hotels, into destinations in themselves. The more a hotel has to offer, the more popular it will be. The spa is the perfect place for people to spend a lot of money. In the next twenty-five years cosmetic surgery alone will become enormous business. Think of what a hotel like this could offer – alternative medicines, ancient healing practices, nips and tucks... All in a beautiful historic town."

For a while she continued to foist her sales pitch on me, laced with an array of figures about visitor numbers, pharmaceutical uptake and other statistics garnered from and beyond the World Health Organisation. However much she may have been right in what she was saying, I could not help thinking of the noisome buildings around me, and how much money and effort it would take to get them back on their feet, let alone encourage tourists to come here.

"It would need the commitment of one of the big European or American hotel groups to take it by the scruff of the neck," I said.

"Not necessarily. The voucher scheme is a chance for locals and anyone else to run the business."

"You think they are up to it?"

"I am going to put money on it."

"You're not a local."

"There are ways of doing these things."

Fernande was annoying me. My ego was bruised. I had come here knowing about business, knowing better than she how finance in the new Czech Republic was carried on, expecting to offer *gratis* advice that would otherwise cost hundreds, even thousands of pounds, yet she had absolutely no interest in soliciting my opinion. When the fruit dumplings arrived I asked her how much she was putting in.

"Everything." She was defiant.

"Everything?" I looked at Sophie, who gave a Gallic shrug. I turned back to Fernande. It was time to name names. "Where does Alexei Machinek fit in?"

"I need somebody here who knows how everything works."

That was all. I waited to see if she was going to throw any further light on how exactly he was going to achieve this, and when she didn't I gave up, sat back and smiled. "Well, it sounds wonderful. A great idea. I wish you the best of luck."

Then I changed the subject.

The next morning after breakfast Sophie and I went for a stroll in the grounds. Bristol Palace and its co-hotels, Villa Kralovska, Villa Teresa and Villa Livia, were all classic *fin-de-siècle* châteaux set in a large park, with tracks leading off into the forests all around. We had sat up late discussing the buyout of this complex. Sophie's grandparents had recently died, and Fernande must now be worth a few million pounds, though it was not the loss of her own potential inheritance that Sophie was concerned about, as much as the thought of her mother making a fool of herself.

As Sophie took my arm and propelled me into the gardens, I

realised that these must have been the very paths that Sigmund Freud had walked more than ninety years earlier, and I mentioned what my brother James had said about Eddie Bernays and his Viennese uncle. Public relations was Sophie's business, and it turned out that she knew about the Father of Spin; in fact, she now told me, *Propaganda* had been on her university curriculum.

"James didn't have much good to say about him," I said. "He blames him for the wars in South America."

"Well, he is right, but Bernays' first coup was turning public opinion in America around so that they would join the Allies in the First World War. Hill and Knowlton did just the same thing for the Kuwaiti government to get the West to start the Gulf War. '*First demonise the opposition, then appeal to emotions over facts.*' People don't have to swallow it."

"But they do."

"If the PR is any good they do."

At that moment, Sophie tugged at my arm. A man in a black track suit was jogging down the path towards us. He was much as she had described him; a solidly built Russian, with short grey hair, out-of-season tan and a fluid running style that showed he had always been pretty fit.

"*Ahoj, michka!*" Perspiration was running down his forehead as he continued jogging on the spot.

"*Guten Morgen, Herr Machinek.*" Sophie was never able entirely to hide her displeasure. "*Das ist mein Partner Tom.*"

"*Hallo Tom. Kommen Sie aus Deutschland?*"

"I'm English."

"English? Good. Good spa, eh?"

"Very good."

"Very good." And he was off again, patting me in the back as he departed. Machinek, it turned out, spoke only Russian and German, the language in which he had conducted his business with Sophie's mother. He hadn't stopped long enough to appreciate my Russian linguistic skills. One day he would wish that he had.

Sophie declined my offer of a day in Prague, electing instead to stay behind to keep an eye on her mother. My contacts in the city were not particularly useful in coming up with any information on Alexei Machinek. There were plenty of no-good adventurers swimming in the shark-infested waters of Czech capitalism, however much the government tried to keep a grip on the country's finances. The currency was on the verge of becoming fully convertible and my company had a deal going through with a brewery that was being bought out by a British client. I managed to get twenty minutes with the British Commercial Attaché to hear his take on the latest events. There were bound to be Russians in Karlsbad, he said. Without much seaside, and with a love of saunas, they had always gone for spas; they probably had sufficient connections to buy up whatever property they wanted, even though it would make a mockery of the voucher scheme.

"Pretty much anything goes now," he said. "The house in Pribor where Sigmund Freud was born has just opened as a massage parlour."

At the end of the day I touched base with the London office. There was a message from a financier in Moscow I had called before I left. Machinek, it turned out, had been a minor official in the Soviet Ministry of Labour. Nothing else.

The weather cheered up while I was in Karlsbad, and so did Sophie. She had started to try some of the cures and pronounced them not so bad after all. Machinek was still in town. So, apparently, was Havel, whom she had seen in the street.

"I wanted to talk to him," she said, "but I couldn't think of anything to say. I wish I'd seen one of his plays."

On my last day I returned from Prague in mid-afternoon and, finding no one around, decided I should attempt to appreciate the spa before I left. A sauna seemed the most benign of the treatments, and it was the only one I was familiar with. The trip was coming to an end and I was feeling something of a failure, but Fernande was old enough to do as she pleased and I resigned myself to thinking that there was little I could do. After a good steaming, I went into the cool room, where I lay down on a wooden bench and drifted off to sleep. Consciousness returned through a half-dream, a babel of foreign languages that turned out to be Russian. Keeping my eyes closed, I imagined two men in towels, one of them Alexiei Machinek.

In a low murmur, punctuated by harsh laughter, they told me what I wanted to know. They were talking about the government's distribution of vouchers for the sale of the hotels, which was due to take place in a few weeks' time. Names were mentioned, Czech names. The recipients were clearly going to receive a knock on the door and a request to buy their vouchers. If they refused, there was no doubt what would happen to them. This would go beyond coercion and intimidation. With excited chuckles the two steaming Muscovites recalled cases of violence to former non-compliant victims, though the names they mentioned here were all Russian. "*Remember the cat in Liv's incinerator?*" "*It was the first year Sergei's cherry trees didn't blossom.*" "*Nikolayev's dascha went under the wheels like a cardboard box...*"

I didn't catch all of it but I heard enough. My eyes remained closed until they were leaving, when I peeked just to make sure it was Machinek. That evening I told Sophie what I had heard. She was thoughtful but not too surprised.

"So they are going to buy up all the hotels' vouchers," she surmised, "whether people want to sell or not, using any kind of coercion to get their way…"

"With your mother's money. We'll have to tell her."

"Why should she believe us? She'll probably think we're making it up; she knows we're against the whole thing. Anyway, we don't have any proof."

She was right. It was hard to know what to do, but one thing was for certain: I couldn't extend my stay any longer. There was pressing work in London and I had to get back. We didn't sleep much that night. In fact I didn't think I had slept at all until I turned over in bed to find Sophie gone. It was six-thirty in the morning. The serious guests, including Sophie's mother, were up every day at six to start their treatment. Twenty minutes later I was dressed and in the gardens, where I found Sophie returning from a walk. There was a bounce in her step and a glint in her dark eyes.

"I'm hungry." She kissed me on the lips. "Let's have breakfast."

At the buffet she stacked her plate with cold meats, cheese, black bread and jam, and as we settled down at a table she took out a notebook. She wanted details of everything I had heard in the sauna.

"It's only my word," I said. "And they haven't actually done anything yet. We don't have any hard facts to got on, nothing to take to the authorities."

"Don't forget I'm in public relations," she said. "We don't deal in facts."

"Ah, I see. So first you will…"

"Demonise the enemy…"

"Alexei Machinek is the villain. And then…"

"Use emotion instead of truth. I had a brain storm on the path this morning. It was like a cerebral irrigation, a Freudian enema. It must be something to do with this place – I was probably walking on exactly the same path the Father of Psychoanalysis took with the Father of Spin. I suddenly saw the way through. We know the psychology; all it needs now is a little engineering."

We talked for a long time about how her campaign might go, who might have the list of potential voucher holders and who might be worth talking to in town without rousing suspicions. Sophie wondered if Václev Havel was still there.

I wished her luck with her campaign, left her to it and flew back to London.

A couple of days after her mother had driven back to Geneva, Sophie returned home. This had given her sufficient time on the ground to start her campaign, which she then continued to run from her office. It wasn't long before lurid stories began to appear in the European Press about Russian mafia cartels that were buying up hotels in Eastern Europe and turning them into whore houses, money-laundering gaming palaces and vicious vice dens. Rumours circulated that one of these mafia outfits was run by a gang that used to be part of the Soviet Ministry of Labour. It had a history of violence that included the abduction of pets and children and nobody would be surprised if they had eaten the odd baby.

Soon afterwards Sophie heard that Andrei Machinek had been sent packing. She was elated, and so was the company she worked for, because in the course of her campaigning she had met Havel and picked up some business from the Czech government. They weren't high payers, but her company was happy to give the fledgling democracy some added spin. Her career was looking up.

Over a celebratory *dim sum* at the Royal China, we wondered what Fernande would make of Machinek's sudden disappearance.

"She'll get over it," said Sophie. "And Pappa will never know."

"And what *we* may never know was why Fernande ever decided to put all her money into such a scheme in the first place without telling Patrice. I still wonder if he hadn't hurt her in some way and she was trying to get back at him."

"Perhaps she really did want to do something different with her life. She might have been right about spas – since I've been back, the papers seem to be full of them. If Machinek hadn't been a crook, it might have worked."

"You're kidding." I still felt resentment that Fernande had not wanted any advice from me. "Nobody's ever going to pay good money for some cranky treatment, getting covered in seaweed or mud – you can do it for nothing down on the beach. The great days of spas went out of fashion with the Edwardians. They'll never take off again."

Sophie looked at me warily and shook her head.

Since she left me, there has been nobody to tell me I'm wrong.

3: THE ACTRESS AND THE EARL-BISHOP

Hotel Bristol
Capri, Bay of Naples, Italy
www.hotelbristolcapri.com

Although I knew about the Earl-Bishop's friendship with Sir William Hamilton, British Envoy to the Court of the Two Sicilies, and his love of Naples, I didn't get around to visiting the region until after Sophie had left me, more than half a dozen years after our adventures in the Czech Republic. Even then, I didn't quite make the journey I had intended. I was looking for a hotel that might kick-start a new relationship and the Bay of Naples, where hotels called Bristol are scattered like flotsam, seemed just the sort of place. There is a two-star Bristol in the city, but what I had in mind was the Edwardian splendour promised by an old Art Nouveau poster I had found, which proclaimed: "*Hôtel Bristol Naples, Prop. A. Landry. Leading and most complete hotel sumptuously renovated in 1902 – bathroom adjoining each apartment –winter garden – homely residence.*"

This Hotel Bristol was at 168 Corso Vittorio Emanuele in the sought-after Posillipo district of the city where Sir William lived and where his own residence had briefly become a hotel. Half a century later, in 1865, Sr Landry's Hotel Bristol had been built as a palace by an architect named Semeraro and by 1896 it was in Baedaeker's hotel listing as being in a "*healthy position with magnificent views*". The First World War deprived it of customers and profit, however, and in 1917 it was turned into apartments. To my delight I discovered that one of them, "Casa 12" on the second floor, now offered bed and breakfast.

I had been in no rush to start an affair after Sophie had left, but people are unsettled at the thought of friends and relations being single and my brother James took it upon himself to act as talent scout. I was sitting at my parents' home in southern Spain, nursing my sorrows and reading some of my father's old guide books, when he sent me a text message: *1 4 U*. The small screen on my mobile phone glowed with a picture of a woman who looked happy and bright. It was just a snapshot of her head and shoulders, so I had no sense of her height or figure or dress sense, but she was attractive with dark hair and a knowing look. I texted back to tell Jamers to dispatch her *2 me 4thwith*.

Nathalie's unseen qualities turned out to be just fine. She was a talkative, single-minded woman, who was flying high in the management of the NHS. The affair began swiftly, and she commented on how digital photography and the internet had made blind dates a thing of the past. It was, she thought, a very 21st-century way of meeting. On the contrary, I said, this was just how the aristocracy used to meet, though instead of sending digital images through the ether, they sent canvases by messengers across land and sea. This was how Sir William Hamilton had been tempted to take on Emma Hart, a woman who turned everyone's heads, and certainly would have turned mine.

"*Emma's creation betokened a glorious mood in her Creator,*" Lord Bristol, Bishop of Derry, declared, and in a letter to her he wrote:

Oh, Emma who'd ever be wise

If madness be loving of thee?

In 1780, the most expensive bed to be had in London was in the Temple of Health in the Royal Terrace of the Adelphi. Overlooking the Thames, this development by the siblings John, Robert, James and William Adam had been completed half a dozen years earlier, taking its name from the Greek *adelphoi*, meaning brothers, Greek being all the rage since Sir William Hamilton's fabulous collection of Greek vases had recently arrived at the British Museum to form the basis of an Antiquities Department. The Hellenic theme continued inside the Temple of Health, with statuary and live goddesses exotically draped and more or less enrobed. The enterprise was organised by a Scottish showman quack by the name of Dr James Graham, who lectured on procreation while his acolytes sung, recited and posed as figures from antiquity. The high point of this farrago was the "magnetico-electric pathway to Elysian love-making" involving the Great Celestial State Bed, which couples could hire for fifty pounds a night. Twelve feet long and nine feet wide, this opulent vehicle where "perfect babies could be created" stood beneath a heavenly blue canopy supported by forty glass pillars. The exotic atmosphere was plumped up with pillows and quilts and suffused with perfumes and music while beneath the bed The Hauksbee Influence Machine, a glass sphere that crackled with primitive electricity, supplied the necessary celestial fire.

One of the most popular of Dr Graham's goddesses was the teenage Emma Hart, who posed as Hygeia, goddess of health, and romped naked in mud baths, treatment the doctor believed could prolong patients' lives. Indeed, he may have invented the mud pack, but for all his ingenuity his success was short-lived. The Temple moved briefly to Pall Mall and lowered the price of its bed, but it lost money and closed in 1784, whereupon the doctor returned to Scotland, discovered religion and died of starvation aged 49, shortly after publishing a pamphlet entitled *How to Live for Many Weeks or Months or Years Without Eating Anything Whatsoever*.

Needless to say, Dr Graham's emporium attracted all the rakes in town, and Emma soon became mistress to the elderly and roguishly named Sir Harry Fetherstonhaugh, master of Uppark in Sussex. Now a National Trust property, the mansion contains the dining table on which the Cheshire blacksmith's daughter would dance for Sir Harry and his guests, who no doubt thought her a charming young thing.

In fine aristocratic style, when Sir Harry caused Emma, still aged only sixteen, to become pregnant, he threw her out. One of Uppark's appreciative house guests, Sir Charles Greville, came to the rescue, taking her into his care and his bed in Paddington Green in west London, while Emma's bastard child was packed off to her relations in Wales. Though well connected, Greville was not particularly rich, and he saw in Emma the opportunity of making money by commissioning the artist George Romney R.A. to make portraits of her, which he could turn into lithographs and flog around town, or at least around London's fast set. Romney was soon hooked, and made scores of paintings and studies of his new muse. Circe, Medea, Thetis… Emma played all the parts, her full figure bursting through diaphanous blouses, her chestnut hair loose, her feet naked, her head to one side and her knowing, flirtatious brown eyes following you to every corner of the room.

At this point Sir William Hamilton, Greville's fifty-three-year-old uncle, turned up. Suddenly widowed, he had brought his wife's body back to London for burial, and here he met Emma, who had become devoted to his nephew. Hamilton had no children and Greville was his closest relation, and thus his potential heir, a situation that could change should he marry again. It was a good bet that if Sir William took up with working-class Emma, however, the chances of his marrying would be slim, reducing the possibility of any legitimate progeny.

More charitable people might suggest that Greville was making a supreme sacrifice, for though Emma had become deeply attached to him he appeared more concerned for the happiness of his distinguished and beloved uncle in his twilight years than he was for himself. Whatever the motive, shortly after Hamilton returned to Naples Greville put his plan into action, sending his uncle a portrait of Emma as Bacchante, a *memento vive*, and suggesting that she went to stay with him for six months. In the letter that contained this proposal, he wrote, "*Emma is the only woman I have slept with without offending my senses, and a cleaner, sweeter bedfellow does not exist.*"

Emma and her mother arrived in that intoxicating permanent summer that is Naples in April 1786, and under the feathered comfort of Sir William's wing, she learned the piano, French, Italian and the ways of Neapolitan society to an extent that she would soon become the favourite confidante of Queen Maria Carolina who ruled the kingdom while her husband went boar hunting. Sir William's kindness was rewarded with *tableaux vivants* and "attitudes" that would make any man happy. Goethe was one of many famous visitors to appreciate Emma's gifts. "*After many years of devotion to the arts and the study of nature,*" he wrote in *Italian Journeys,* "*Hamilton has found the acme of these delights in the person of an English girl of twenty with a beautiful face and perfect figure... she lets down her hair and, with a few shawls, gives so much variety to her poses, gestures, expressions etc, that the spectator can hardly believe his eyes... as a performance, it's like nothing you ever saw in your life before.*"

News that his old friend had a new mistress brought the Bishop of Derry scuttling down from Rome. Born the same year, Lord Bristol and Sir William began their lifelong friendship at Westminster School in London and it continued through Bristol's visits to Naples and a regular exchange of letters. Bristol had first visited Naples while Sir William's wife was alive, when he was confined to bed after getting too close to the erupting lava of Mount Vesuvius. Ideas of art and nature stimulated the two men's continuing friendship.

In Emma, Bristol found more than art and nature, however; he found a soul mate. Flamboyant, quick-witted, she must have ignited sparks to fly between them in the sunny drawing room of the refined and tolerant Hamilton. Dressed in the purple gaters and regalia of a protestant bishop, fresh faced and with a reckless eye, Bristol would have been in the front row of any gathering to watch Emma's attitudes. And if the major-domo had not taken his wide brimmed hat of office from him on arrival, he would have thrown it in the air with a whoop of hallelujahs when her last turn was done.

"*That he should admire her beauty and her wonderful attitudes is not singular,*" Lady Holland later wrote, "*but that he should like her society certainly is, as it is impossible to go beyond her in vulgarity and coarseness.*"

Marie Élizabeth-Louise Vigée-LeBrun, the celebrated French court painter whose portrait of Bristol still hangs at Ickworth, found Emma an exceptional model and she painted her three times, but she, too, found the young *arriviste* to be coarse, unintel-ligent and "*exceedingly mocking and denigrating to the point that these faults were her only conversation*".

Coarseness can be the language of flirtation, a language in which the Earl-Bishop was fluent, and it is safe to say that Emma was more of a man's woman than a woman's woman. Her coarseness was also suggested by her accent, which had arrived via London and Wales and was described by Bristol as "dearest Emma's Dorick dialect". Mimicry can be included among Bristol's accomplishments, and as to mockery and denigration, the actress and the bishop we re a matching pair. "*Lively in carriage and manners, quick in speech, blunt, sometimes even rude,*" was how Goethe described him. "*It was sometimes his whim to be offensive, but if one treated him equally offensively he would become perfectly amenable.*"

Bristol found Emma "*senza paragone*" and he corresponded with her for the rest of his life, anticipating his visits to Naples with "*the same eagerness that the Jews wait for Our Lord*". Closing his letters with "*sweetest Emma, adieu!*" he wrote: "*I am the second letter of your alphabet, though you are the first in mine.*" As for Emma, she wrote that "*le bon et bienfaissant*" Bristol was very fond of her, very kind and very entertaining.

In spite of his flirtations with Emma, the bishop was always supportive of her relationship with Sir William and he even offered to officiate at the couple's wedding. Wisely, perhaps, Sir William chose a less controversial prelate to conduct their marriage in St George's Church, Hanover Square, five years after her appearance in Naples. She was twenty-six and growing plump; he was sixty-one, and the biggest scandal of their lives had not yet begun.

Emma and the bishop were very much in my own thoughts as the plane descended over the Bay of Naples. The water glinted now as it had glinted for them; Vesuvius, clearly visible, still dominated the scene; the names of Emma and Sir William Hamilton would be on the lips of the tour guides leading the troops from the massive cruise ships. I had searched the internet and elsewhere to find out all I could about the couple prior to our holiday, so that I would have something to talk about. Ninety per cent of the success of all speeches, as I am frequently telling people, is in the spade work done beforehand, and I believe ordinary social conversation benefits from a little homework, too. It was the first time that Nathalie and I had spent more than a night or so in each other's company, and though I was not convinced that the relationship was going to last, I wanted to give it my best shot.

Nathalie's response to my eulogising about Emma Hamilton was to say that she sounded "a bit pushy", which only confirmed my view that Emma had not been a woman's woman. But Nathalie liked to dance herself, she said, though her high-flying job left her with little time or opportunity. I suggested that we might try to catch a flavour of Emma's poses by going to see the erotic paintings from Pompeii in the National Archaeological Museum in Naples, where, as I understood it, the original Bacchantes could be seen dancing in a way that anybody of taste and sensitivity could appreciate. Nathalie said that if I wanted to see that sort of thing they probably had porn channels in the hotel.

As it had turned out, we were not staying in the city. Nathalie had not liked the sound of Posillipo's Casa 12, even when I explained my interest in all things Bristol. "I'm not having a hotel without a pool or a nearby beach," she said. Before I could come up with an alternative, she had phoned to say that she had tracked down five other hotels Bristol around the Bay of Naples: one in Sorrento ("too big"), one in Pompeii ("too far away"), two in Ischia ("wherever that is") and one in Capri ("which I've booked – the penthouse suite").

The Capri Bristol was a handsome terracotta-coloured villa set on a clifftop with steps going down to a small beach. It had just seventeen rooms, a solarium, hot-tub and garden. Our rooftop suite had two bedrooms, a lounge and a wonderful terrace directly above the Marina Grande. At Nathalie's request I used her mobile phone to take a couple of pictures of her on the terrace with Vesuvius in the distance across the bay, so she could send them to friends and colleagues with a message: *Wsh u wr hr*. For a few days we did not venture far. The terrace, beach and solarium were all we needed, plus a small bar we found in the Marina. But I am not good at lying still for long, and creeping restlessness was cured by making forays around the island. From the high spots, from Tiberius's villa and the Via Krupp, I stared at the city of Naples at the far side of the bay. There was no getting Nathalie to cross the water to visit the archaeological museum or anything else. I sat in the garden of the five-star Quisisana, where we might have stayed had I not been so obsessed with ticking off Bristols, and drank a toast to Emma Hart.

Nathalie was adventurous in her own way. Being gregarious, she made friends easily and I often returned from my walks to find her engaged in conversation with some of the hotel guests, or even the staff who, incidentally, had no idea how the hotel got its name. In the evenings, we would go to the Marina Grande, where we made many instant holiday acquaintances, not returning to the hotel until late. Nathalie found her feet on the dance floor of a small club, where she put up an impressive show, and on several occasions I willingly stood at the bar while she went through her routine with a more enthusiastic holidaymaker. Unable to keep up the pace, I left her one night with an English party that had come off a yacht in the marina, staggering back to the hotel alone. I realised then, with some relief, that the affair would not last, and I guess that she knew it, too.

But we were on holiday, paid for and promised to, and we were still capable of enjoying each other's company. On the last day we lunched on fish and the local Lacrima Cristi sparkling wine in the hotel and it was clear that we really never were going to get to see the Pompeii erotica. Perhaps I sounded disappointed, I don't know. Anyway, during our siesta in the hotel room, wearing just a sheet, Nathalie gamely attempted a few "attitudes", spinning around the room and even going on to the terrace to dance beneath the sun.

"What do you think?" she called.

"*Senza paragone,*" I replied.

Nathalie was no Emma Hart. Her figure was not full and her hair was on the short side, but I was more than appreciative of her talent. The brutal, obvious moves of the disco floor were replaced with something more intimate, more knowing and assured. Her bare feet followed the rhythms of the notes hummed on her smiling lips, and her lashes flitted over the brown eyes that stayed on me as she moved around the room, whirling and turning and letting slip the sheet, first this way, then that. If I had been a painter I would have been hard pressed to know which pose I would have liked her to hold. I was flattered, delighted, visibly moved. So were several people in the bay below, by the sound of it, for when she took another turn on the terrace whoops came from the yachts anchored off the Marina.

I am not sure if it was Nathalie or Emma whom I loved with such passion that afternoon. But I do know that when the plane once more touched down on damp Luton airport the following day, it was Nathalie I kissed goodbye. Without bitterness or rancour, and without saying anything but "thank you", we both knew that we would not be going on holiday together again.

About a year later I was having a drink with James. Half way through the evening, he asked if I had heard that Nathalie had quit her job and career to go sailing in the Mediterranean. The news pleased me. I was happy for her. She had helped to replenish a little of my self esteem; it is miraculous how beneficial a kind woman can be.

Now I am left with a picture of her, on that last afternoon in the Hotel Bristol in Capri, the sheet struggling to stay on her bronzed body, her brown eyes overflowing with good will towards men, and out to sea the skipper at the helm of a Nicholson 32, with one empty sleeve tucked into his shirt, a patch over his right eye, the left one transfixed on the figure dancing around the terrace of the Hotel Bristol. Small coloured pennants flutter on the halyard: "*England expects every man to do his duty...*"

4: Krupp's Dying Shame

Kempinski Hotel Bristol
Berlin, Germany
www.kempinski-berlin.de

My holiday in Capri and the Bay of Naples led one way and another to Berlin and several coincidental thoughts about society's treatment of women. The following summer I was booked into the Kempinski Bristol in the German capital, attending a conference of Transparency International, an outfit that tries to monitor corruption around the world and encourage probity in business and government. It doesn't actually ferret out malpractice or campaign against it, but simply endeavours, through known cases, to give a regular round-up of what's going on. Finland topped the list of straightest nations that year, Britain was 10th, the USA 16th, Germany 18th. But who knows how far corruption really goes, and in how many hotel rooms dodgy deals have been s t ruck, palms greased, blackmailers and backhanders paid and hotel bills taken care of? Nobody can guess the half of it.

The Kempinski Bristol looks much too smart to be involved in such shenanigans. Tainted with neither scandal nor a mite of dust, this cool 1950s building is a shining white curving box with impeccable lines and orderly rows of square windows in its 301 rooms. It stands on the Kurfürstendamm, Berlin's most animated street, and from my second-floor window I could gaze out at the world going by, though the double glazing was so efficient it sometimes seemed as if I was watching a silent movie. The city has many layers, and I sensed that beneath its cleanliness and culture lay a strong sexual edge. This may be because of the inhabitants' penchant for leatherwear, or the annual Love Parade, which I had just missed, or the naked sunbathers in the

Tiergarten, or the street walkers who look so classy they could be mistaken for rich society women on shopping sprees. *The Blue Angel* and *Cabaret* made Berlin the last word in decadence, a reputation it had fostered since Lord Bristol's day.

The Prussian correctness and moral rectitude embodied in the figure of King Frederick the Great was dissipated during the reign of his nephew and successor, the pleasure-loving Frederick Wilhelm II, who came to the throne in 1786, married twice and lived in Schloss Charlottenburg with several children as well as passing mistresses. His greatest love, however, was for Wilhelmina Encke, a Berlin inn-keeper's daughter who had become his principal dalliance when she was fifteen, had borne him two children and exerted influence over him for the rest of his life. Her humble background and meteoric career matched Emma Hamilton's, so perhaps it was no surprise that Lord Bristol, who was on amicable terms with the king, fell ridiculously in love with Wilhelmina on their first meeting at a concert in Munich in 1795, when he was heading for the Prussian court after visiting the Hamiltons. He was then sixty-four, she was forty-two and described as being a classic beauty with a splendid physique, good humoured and a brilliant conversationalist.

Appropriately for these tales of hotels, Wilhelmina had married a servant at the Prussian court by the name of Johann Friedrich Ritz, and was therefore at this time known as Madame Ritz. Cultured, attractive, she had travelled to Italy to study art and buy paintings for the royal households while improving her health after a failed affair with a young Irish peer, Henry Montague Upton, Viscount Templetown, whom the king had as a consequence driven from Berlin. Erudite, compelling, flattering, entertaining, the Earl-Bishop convinced her that a visit to Naples would do wonders for her health. Appreciative of his attentiveness and cheered by the company of another Irish peer, she warmed to the idea. There was, however, one obstacle. Queen Maria Caroline of Naples would not have a commoner among the court circles in which Bristol and the Hamiltons moved.

When news of this reached Berlin, the king, still in the thrall of Wilhelmina, annulled her marriage to Herr Ritz and created her Countess von Lichtenau in order for the trip to go ahead.

In the salons and on the streets of Naples, the Bishop and the Countess were a scandal to behold, the old reprobate in his sumptuous prelate's purple now adorned with a miniature of the Countess at the end of a gold chain, as if it were a rosary, arm in arm with this attractive, cultured woman more than twenty years his junior. The couple seemed to do everything to encourage rumours but it is unlikely that they ever shared a bed, which was where the aging Bristol found himself at the end of their stay, laid low with a fever and unable to accompany Wilhelmina back to Berlin.

"The good and kindly Lord Bristol is in despair without you," Emma Hamilton wrote to the Countess after her departure, and, using his increasingly overworked cliché, *"He awaits you with the same ardent desire as the Jews the Messiah."*

By this time Lord Bristol was estranged from his wife. One bleak day in November 1782 he had rowed with Elizabeth while out for a drive at Ickworth. Nobody knows what the argument was about. These last furious words between them were overheard by the coachman who took their contents with him to the grave. Bristol promptly left for Ireland, then the Continent, and never returned to England or saw Elizabeth again. However, throughout his travels he continued to bombard Ickworth with works of art and instructions to architects, while Elizabeth endured the never ending building work on her home in desperate isolation. *"I leave him to Heaven,"* she wrote, *"and to those thorns that in his bosom lodge to prick and sting him."*

Bristol soon had other marriages on his mind. He and Wilhelmina began to conspire to elevate his youngest son Frederick into the ranks of minor European aristocracy by marrying him to Countess Mariana von der Mark, her seventeen-year-old daughter by Frederick Wilhelm II, and the king's favourite child. Bristol, the king, his mistress, the fair Countess Mariana von der Mark – everyone was in agreement over the plan. A painter in Dresden was commissioned to paint three full-length pictures of Mariana to dispatch to Frederick, and the marriage would have gone ahead to loud huzzhas, except that Frederick Hervey had not been taken into account. He had no wish to marry the king's daughter since he was in love with Marie Upton, the sister of Wilhelmina's former *amorato* Viscount Templetown. Foiled, outraged, Bristol tried to enlist the help of his favourite daughter, Lady Elizabeth Foster, then living at Chatsworth in a scandalous *ménage à trois* with Georgiana, the Duchess of Devonshire, and her husband, the 5th Duke. It was to no avail.

And so the dizzying merry-go round slowed to a halt.

The following year the King of Prussia died after being nursed through his last illness by Wilhelmina. Neither she nor Emma Hamilton was allowed to survive in society without the protection of their men. When their lovers expired, the glitter of their life was snatched from them. Wilhelmina was imprisoned and her possessions confiscated, just as Emma was abandoned to penury and the debtors' prison on the death of Nelson. Lord Bristol died two years before Emma's most famous lover was killed at the Battle of Trafalgar, but he had no excuse for washing his hands of Wilhelmina during her fall from grace.

Hypocrisy in high places still had a long way to go. The kingdom of Prussia came to an end in 1871 with the creation of modern Germany, and in 1888 Wilhelm II became the last king of Prussia and the first German emperor. In his plumed hats and shining boots, the Kaiser lived for pageants and demonstrations of national strength; during his reign the country became an industrial powerhouse and a showcase of military might. Berlin was one of the largest manufacturing centres in Europe, while the world's largest armament's factory was to be found in Essen, 250 miles to the west. It had a workforce of 24,000. For four hundred years the firm had been owned and run by the local Krupp family. It was now headed by Friedrich Alfred "Fritz" Krupp, who supplied weapons, warships and armour plating to a score of nations based on a policy of *Schutz- und Trutzwaffen* – a one-company arms race in which Krupp pitted countries against each other as he sold impenetrable nickel-steel armour, then chrome shells that could pierce it, then an improved armour that could protect against the chrome shells, then explosive shells that would shatter the improved armour, and so on, rachetting up the world's arms race. The Kaiser loved Krupp and the powerful products that were rapidly expanding his war machinery, and he invited him to join his Privy Council in Berlin.

When Krupp visited the capital, he stayed at the Bristol Hotel, which was then at No 5 Unter den Linden. There he would entertain politicians, businessmen and the nobility, most notably on one occasion with a banquet for two hundred and fifty attended by the Kaiser. He was the hotel's most prestigious and welcome guest. But Krupp had a chronic weight problem and banquets gave him no great pleasure. He was short-sighted, too, and in spite of his successful sales policy, did not think himself a natural hard-headed businessman. As a child he had tried to escape the demands of his father by joining the army, but his physical condition, worsened by asthmatic attacks, soon sent him home again. He married Margarethe Freun von Ende, and their daughter Bertha gave her name to the 43-ton Big Bertha cannons used in the First World War.

A lifelong interest in natural history and a wish to escape cold winters led Krupp, in 1898, to take two yachts equipped for marine research to southern Italy where they would be put at the disposal of Naples' famous aquarium run by the German Darwinian enthusiast, Dr Anton Dhorn. Krupp and his entourage chose Capri as their seasonal base, settling into a whole floor of the Quisisana (the name means "Here, you will be healthy"), which had been opened as a sanatorium by a Scots doctor some years earlier, and was now a thriving hotel in local hands, with its own cows and poultry producing fresh vitals in its extensive grounds.

Krupp's largesse won him many friends on the island, and it

brought him an honorary citizenship, too. He built the Via Krupp, a delightful path cut in the rock giving views at every turn and connecting the Quisisana to the Marina Piccolo where he kept his yachts, Puritan and Maia. Krupp bought the Gardens of Augustus, land with Roman remains, fully conscious that he was stepping into the shoes of the Emperor Tiberius, who retired to the island in 27AD and idled away his life in sexual excess with young boys and even, it was rumoured, being pleasured by suckling babes.

What was good for the Roman emperor was good enough for Krupp, who, beneath the balmy Mediterranean skies allowed his appetite for young men to grow and prosper. In the strange bubble in which his wealth and station kept him, he felt impervious to criticism. At orgies in an island cave, which he described as "a holy place of a secret fraternity of devout mystics", he handed out specially made gold badges, some in the shape of artillery shells, some with crossed forks, for boys who had treated him especially well and one can only guess at their meaning. Sometimes, it was rumoured, sky-rockets were launched when he ejaculated.

Returning home, Krupp found the cold lands of the north lacked excitement, so to keep up his sunny disposition, he asked Conrad Uhl, proprietor of the Hotel Bristol in Berlin, to employ some of his Capri protégés as hotel staff on the condition that when he was in town they would be excused all other duties to attend the Cannon King, who would pay all their wages. Though willing to indulge his most important guest's whims, Uhl already had his suspicions about Krupp, who often stayed alone in the hotel even though he was in town with his wife. When the first contingent of young Capri lads arrived, the proprietor was irritated to find that they spoke no other language but Italian and had neither the ability nor the inclination to buckle to the formal discipline of a top German hotel. And when Krupp came to Berlin and the young Italians dropped what they were doing to go to his suite, from where the sounds of Capri-style enjoyment erupted, Uhl decided that the matter had gone too far. Such behaviour threatened not only the reputation of the Hotel Bristol, but it might also lead to the loss of liberty of its proprietor, who would have been arraigned along with the culprits should it be known that perverse activities we re going on under his roof. Under article 175 of the Imperial Penal Code of 1871, sodomy could result in a heavy prison sentence with hard labour.

So Conrad Uhl went to see Berlin's Police Commissioner, Hans von Tresckow.

The response he received surprised him. Krupp was not the only senior figure in this manly, militaristic state to be living a double life, Treschow said. There were police files on literally hundreds of people surrounding the Kaiser, from his private secretary and ADCs to his own younger brother, as well as a raft of counts and top military men. Treschow had reports on mass fellatio orgies among the officers of the elite Garde du Corp, and of bizarre evenings when the chief of the Reich's military cabinet put on a tu-tu to dance for appreciative officers. The dossiers had been gathered because a number of blackmail cases had been uncovered, but Tresckow was in no hurry to pull their subjects in, especially such a close friend of the Kaiser as Krupp.

Events began unravelling fast. Stories of Krupp's orgies escaped Capri and started rumours circulating openly in the Italian Press in the summer of 1902. Krupp did not go back to Capri again. Homosexuality was not illegal in Italy, but it was clear he would not be welcome in the country for what was now commonly termed "the German vice".

There was no news of this in Germany until November when the socialist newspaper *Vorwärts* published a story titled KRUPP IN CAPRI. Copies of the paper were seized and Krupp, now a miserable sight and staying with friends, threatened to sue. Anonymous letters and reports from foreign papers were sent to Margherethe Krupp who, in despair, showed them to the Kaiser. She was persuaded to retire to a mental institution in Jena.

There is no evidence of how Fritz Krupp's life ended on November 22. Germany's news agency reported simply that he had died at Villa Hügel, his mansion in Essen, and that death was caused by a stroke. But nobody had been allowed to see the body, which was sealed in a casket. There was no autopsy; all the general rules and procedures surrounding his death we re ignored. Unrepentant, Krupp's last written words were: "*I leave this world without rancour and without bitterness; leave it in peace with all men, including those who have done me the worst wrong.*"

At his funeral, 24,000 respectful Krupp workers lined the streets. The Kaiser himself led the mourners, walking behind the cortège, and afterwards he gave a speech to the firm's management at the railway station prior to his departure, defending Krupp's "*delicate and sensitive nature... that offered the only point to attack through which he might be dealt a mortal blow.*"

The London *Times* reported world opinion: "*The German Emperor's loyalty to Herr Krupp's memory warms American hearts. Says the New York Times: – 'It was a courageous act, which will have an effect all over the world.'*" And it added its own note of indignation: "*Socialism of the Vorwärts stamp with its basis of calumny against private character, is not popular here.*"

Released from the asylum, Margarethe Krupp became involved in the company, setting up a housing benefit scheme that still operates. Under her beneficence, the estate was designed by Georg Metzendorf in the style of an English garden city and was listed in 1987. She lived to be seventy-two, dying in 1931, the year it was completed. You can walk through the attractive Margarethenhöhe housing estate in Essen today.

Teschow's files did not become public knowledge until 1919, after the Kaiser had been defeated by the Allies, in spite of Krupp's guns. By this time the Hotel Bristol had changed its name, just as all things English and French had done during the war, the Westminster Hotel becoming the Station House and the Piccadilly Café being renamed Vaterland. The Bristol was re-named the Conrad Uhl, in honour of its renowned and much put-upon proprietor. After the hotelier's death it continued to be called Conrad Uhl's Hotel Bristol.

Up until this moment there had been no hotels in Kurfürstendamm. It was then a semi-rural street where gardens fronted small houses, but it was becoming the popular place to stroll and to set up shop. In 1926, the Kempinski family of restaurateurs, who had been in business for a quarter of a century, opened their most successful establishment at No 27, serving up to 10,000 customers a day. But the Kempinskis were Jewish and in 1939 the property was confiscated. Allied bombing in 1944 destroyed both the Hotel Bristol in Unter der Linden and the Kempinski restaurant. After the war the sole surviving member of the family, Dr Frederic W. Unger, set about building a hotel on the Kurfürstendamm site. The former owners of the Bristol joined in the new project and the Bristol name was brought back to life.

The Kempinski Bristol opened in 1952 as modern Germany's first five-star hotel. The best hotel in town, it was untainted by any scandal, and as far as I know it still is.

5: Lady Thatcher's Finest Hour

Le Royal Meridien Bristol
Warsaw, Poland
www.lemeridien.com/poland/warsaw

Matt Miller did not approve of my parents after he found out that they had regularly visited Spain while General Franco was still in power. I wonder what he would have said about the plans of the liberal Whig Lord Bristol to tour the peninsula in the reign of the absolutist Carlos IV. I will never find out. When we were in the sixth form Matt was the most politically active person I knew, and the most opinionated. It never occurred to him not to say whatever was on his mind, which didn't make him many friends, but he never cared. To me his honesty was fresh air. He never said anything that hadn't been thought about, or that he could not argue through with an intelligence that was matched by a masochistic integrity. When, for instance, I suggested that a pile of us spent a week down at my parents' villa after our final school exams, he declined as if he were a conscientious objector, and as a result missed a really good time.

We went our separate ways after that. I studied economics at Nottingham; he read political science at London. We caught up again just once, when one of the old school crowd was getting married. The stag party was memorable in a number of ways, not just because a right of passage was being celebrated. It was also the night that the Conservative Cabinet got its knives out for the mass stabbing of Margaret Thatcher, and Matt persuaded us to go to a pub with a television so that we could see the result of the crucial vote that would decide whether she would be in a second round of the leadership election. She had been prime minister so long we could not recall public life without her. The longest serving prime minister in 150 years, Matt said, and he knew exactly how many days she had been in office. Statistics stuck to him like glue, and after going over the ministers' likely voting intentions, one by one, he had made predictions on the outcome. To be honest, I was rather annoyed that the event dominated an evening that had something more important to celebrate, but by the time the result was announced, I was as swept up in the moment as everyone else.

Sophie was the bride's best friend and that was where we met; the first hair-curling glimpse came across the aisle in a rural Norfolk church where the wedding took place. In a silk jacket and with the sun streaming through the stained-glass windows and illuminating her fresh skin, she outshone the bride. At the reception afterwards, I was making headway with her over the champagne, when I introduced her to Matt and the relationship nearly ended before it began.

Without even a simple hello, he said, "I hate church weddings. All that stupid stuff the couple has to say to each other and all the money everyone spends, it's obscene."

"You needn't have come." It was the first time I had witnessed Sophie's cold look, those soft brown eyes petrifying, the jaw tightening, a few muscles twitching in the lovely neck. It was harsh, and if she had been a man I would have stepped out of the room.

Matt didn't notice. "Of course I had to come. I wanted to hear the best man's speech." He laughed. "Besides, the Champagne's free, isn't it?"

She did not take to Matt. He was too loud, too dogmatic, and she attributed his outspokenness to simple social ineptitude. Yet he was very generous, and a few weeks later we heard from the newlyweds that an envelope had been waiting for them in their honeymoon hotel in New York. A note itemised a menu for a full day of excursions in the city, including reservations for lunch and dinner at different restaurants, plus tickets to a musical. Every hour of the day had been accounted for on the detailed itinerary, which had been laid out on an Excel spreadsheet. Sophie said she found this intrusive and it only went to prove that Matt was a "control freak". I thought it was just Matt being Matt.

Moving to Docklands, being so wrapped up in work and travelling a great deal, I didn't see Matt again, though I had always imagined that one day I would open the paper to find that he had been elected the new Labour MP for somewhere or other, or that he was active in a high-profile pressure group. But when his name did eventually find its way into the papers it was in quite a different way. Sophie spotted the story first, in the London *Evening Standard*. Headed THATCHER STALKER CAUGHT, a single paragraph reported the arrest of one Matt Miller who had apparently been bothering the former prime minister. Of course we weren't sure at first if this was our Matt Miller, but later it appeared that it most certainly was. The sentencing took place a few months later, after psychiatric reports. It only merited a small news story, and this probably reflected Thatcher's loss of prestige, which I think also accounts for the fact that most people I tell this story to cannot recall her stalker at all. Anyway, in the end, being of previous good character, Matt was given sixty hours of community service and had to promise not to go within half a mile of Thatcher's home. So that was that.

Half a dozen years later I booked into the Hotel Bristol in Warsaw.

Poland was in the process of joining the EU, and I, or rather the consultancy I worked for, was helping them. My interest in all hotels Bristol was well underway, but I was first alerted to this one when I was doing some background reading about the country's recent history and read Timothy Garton Ash's *The Polish Revolution*, in which the author spent a night in the Warsaw Bristol, "*an establishment of such crumbling grandeur and sublime seediness that it seemed to have been built for Graham Greene. My room had three illuminated call buttons: porter, waitress, shoeboy. I pressed them each in turn. Nobody came. A scraggy cat stalked through the French windows in the dining room. There were cockroaches in the bath.*"

That was in 1980. Just over a decade later, once more back in the capitalist fold, the former Art Nouveau flagship had been spectacularly renovated by Rocco Forte and his sister Olga Polizzi in conjunction with Orbis, the state tourist office, and it was without doubt a Bristol among Bristols and the best that Poland had to offer. More recent owners had named it Le Royal Meridien Bristol and it was relatively inexpensive, even though somebody else was picking up the bill. I had been looking forward to an experience quite unlike that of Garton Ash.

The hotel is centrally situated on the main avenue, The King's Walk, next to the Presidential Palace where the Warsaw Pact was signed in 1952, and just round the corner from the rebuilt Old Town Square. It was also no more than a fifteen-minute stroll from any of the people I had come to advise and do business with. On the first day I returned to my room after six solid hours of meetings, tidied my notes, showered, changed and went down to the clubby Column Bar for a beer while I waited for my hosts to pick me up and take me off somewhere for dinner.

Matt Miller was serving behind the bar. I think I actually shook my head in disbelief, but he seemed quite unfazed and put a hand across the counter to grip mine.

"How are you?" he asked. There was no doubting his own health. His eyes were bright, his hair trim, his barman's bow tie, waistcoat and white apron elegant and there was no fat on him. Somehow, in that first glance, I could see that he was more settled, too.

"Surprised and delighted," I said. "What are you doing here?"

"Pouring drinks. What can I get you, sir?"

It was Happy Hour and several customers needed serving, so I sat on a swivel stool at the bar, snatching conversation between orders. He was living in Warsaw, he said, and had a Polish wife and child, and he spoke passable Polish to the customers. I felt awkward being a guest in this five-star establishment, paying for him to pour my drinks, and when he brought my change on a small silver plate, my hand hovered before scooping it all up, recalling that good socialists disapproved of tips. I asked him if he knew that John and Helen, the couple whose wedding we had attended in Norfolk, had split up, and I tried to think of other tragedies that had happened to me or our mutual friends, just to make him – or more probably me – feel better. Yet he seemed completely at home behind the bar. It certainly wasn't the time to ask him about his misdemeanour with Margaret Thatcher.

My dinner hosts arrived after some fifteen minutes and I gave Matt my room number explaining that I was here for three days, and that I would catch him in the bar some time, perhaps when it wasn't so crowded.

As it turned out, I was hopelessly busy and didn't see him again. On my last night, I arrived back late and headed straight for the Column Bar to say goodbye, but he was not on duty, so I gave the barman my business card and asked him to pass it on to Matt, together with my adieus. Then I went up to my room. It had been a pleasure staying in this premier Bristol, and even though I was happy to have ticked off one more, as usual on leaving I felt a sense of dissatisfaction that I had not made better use of the place. The television was on and I had hogged the internet connection, and taken a couple of beers from the minibar, but I hadn't uncapped my Mont Blanc and penned thoughtful notes to friends on the headed notepaper, or tried any options from the list of services. As for the leisure facilities, I had not even managed a dip in the indoor heated pool. I was thinking about all this as I scooped up all the souvenirs I could and crammed them into my suitcase ready for the morning taxi to the airport when there was a knock. I turned down the volume on the television, opened the door, and in came Matt pushing a trolley with a bottle in an ice bucket.

"Room Service," he said as he swept by me. "Couldn't let you go without a drink."

He uncorked the Champagne, poured out two flutes, and we settled into the leather armchairs from where we raised our glasses. Though it was late and I was tired, I was glad I hadn't missed him. I told him that I had enjoyed my stay at the hotel, which seemed rather like thanking my host for having me. This prompted him to give me a brief history of the place, though of course I had done my own homework. When he started to tell me all about the virtuoso pianist and prime minister Ignacy Paderewski, who was a co-founder of the hotel in 1897, I didn't have the heart to say that a CDs of his Plonia symphony was packed in my suitcase. I had made a point of asking my Polish business hosts for recommendations of recordings of this national hero to buy as souvenirs, which had helped to ingratiate myself with them. I would write it off as legitimate business expenses.

As Matt talked about the history of the hotel, I stifled a yawn. I had eaten well at the Artibus restaurant, one of the best in town – crab-stuffed chicken and cherry dumplings, with a cigar afterwards in the piano bar – and my pleasure at seeing Matt again had blotted out any memory of his more boorish qualities, which were now beginning to show themselves. Or perhaps time had made me less tolerant. Of course, he was probably on nights, and was only half way through his day. I was in danger of nodding off, when the name of Margaret Thatcher went off like an alarm clock. Blinking, I resurfaced from my reverie.

"She was coming to the end of an extraordinary week," he was saying. His eyes were bright and he was leaning forward. "An extraordinary week. She was like a steamroller. Nobody could stop her. She arrived in a suit of red and gold, with pearls in her ears like small globes. She looked like Elizabeth I, surrounded by courtiers."

I had missed the first few vital words that introduced this topic but I didn't want to go back to the beginning, to admit that my mind had drifted elsewhere, or in any way delay discovering the truth behind the stalking story. So I, too, leaned forward in my chair, hoping that some crumb of information would explain how we had moved on to this crucial subject.

"Of course she and Dennis had the Paderewski suite," he went on. "Unfortunately it's occupied at the moment or I would have shown you around. It's fantastic. I tried to get it for my honeymoon. Anyway, they had it for two nights."

The story could go on no longer without some key facts. "I'm sorry," I said, "when exactly was this again?"

"April 19, 1993. The official opening of the new hotel was due to coincide with the sixtieth anniversary of the Warsaw ghetto uprising. That's why I was here, with my parents."

"That must have been about two years before… before I read about you and Thatcher…"

He cut me off with a dismissive wave as he picked up the Champagne bottle to refill my glass. His eyes glistened, and his face hardened. Now he sat on the edge of the chair; his whole manner had changed. No longer relaxed, he was stroking an ear lobe with one hand while the other rubbed his thigh. He was getting excited; I knew the signs.

"And Kosovo was about to erupt. A *holo*caust, she called it." He put the emphasis on the first syllable just as I imagine Thatcher herself would have done. "She said that she never thought she would see another holocaust in her life. She never believed the world would allow one to happen again. It couldn't and it mustn't, she told them. But of course she was out of office and could do nothing but sit back and watch in horror as John Major, Bill Clinton, the EU, the UN *et al* did absolutely sweet Fanny Adams. 'Spineless', she called them…"

Quivering, he fell silent, and though I could not quite think what Kosovo had to do with anything, I was not immediately tempted to ask. He was looking straight at me with a defiance that made me wary. For a moment I began to believe that it was not really the Matt I knew lurking behind those fiery dark eyes.

I took a gulp of Champagne and ventured, "What did she do?"

"You don't remember?" His eye b rows shot up; he was disappointed in me.

"Perhaps I was… abroad."

"Well, of course, she had to do something. This was Margaret Thatcher, not someone who just lies down and watches injustice triumph. She knew that arming the Muslims was the only way. The only way. And she couldn't keep quiet about it. You know, she had promised Dennis after she had stepped down as prime minister that she wouldn't interfere but it was not in her nature to see something wrong and not try to do whatever she could about it, and in the end even Dennis was supportive." His voice lowered and he sounded not like a fan, but a best friend divulging intimate knowledge. "He knew how upset she was, and he hated to see her so angry. Simply hated it. So she got on the phone to the newsrooms of both BBC and ITV and told them they had to interview her. They had to give this other point of view. All this dithering had to stop."

Pinned down by this passionate tirade in defence of the woman we had so long excoriated, I felt a growing alarm. What about the woman who had destroyed British industry, who had emasculated the miners and set out to destroy the economy of a fledgling democratic Russia as a matter of policy? I looked around the room to see if I could locate those bells that Garton Ash had pushed. Perhaps there would be people on the end of them this time. Meanwhile I also began to recall Thatcher surfacing into the limelight to the fury of John Major and his Cabinet colleagues, but I still couldn't quite recall the sequence of events, or indeed what exactly all the events were.

"And this was in April 1993," I said vaguely, hoping that just by saying the date it might jog my own memory in some way.

Matt turned his attention briefly towards the mute television set. Explosions were erupting in some desert environment. He frowned as he continued to press his hands down his thighs like a woman smoothing her skirt. His voice was level now, as if he were giving a briefing. "The West had had the whole of the Easter weekend to think about deploying NATO planes and they had done nothing. Nothing. Every hour the situation was getting worse. People had been going to see the former prime minister for weeks, asking her to use her influence, but she was powerless to act. Can you imagine how frustrated she felt? All that was needed was a green light from the world's governments and something could have been done. But every hour that passed with their cowardly lack of resolve encouraged Milosevic further. He was about to murder 20,000 Muslims and nobody was doing anything about it."

It was so hard to remember, so many years later, the exact background to Kosovo and all the other events of the Balkans conflict. "She couldn't convince them?" I asked.

He snorted. "They call her the Iron lady. They love that name here in Warsaw and they gave her such a warm welcome when she visited. She adores the Poles, because they are so industrious, and because they have had such a struggle. She was incredibly sympathetic to their terrible history, to their suffering first under the Nazis and then under the Soviets. But in the end, Iron Lady or not, she was still a woman and that means nobody would take her seriously." He sniffed in disgust.

I had to protest. "I'm sure she was taken seriously." It was hard to know how to take all this. "We certainly used to take her seriously when we went on those marches and made those protests…"

He ignored me. "If a man expresses strong feelings about something, he is said to be 'passionate' about it. When a woman shows strong feelings, she is 'emotional', a word that implies instability. Margaret Thatcher's plans for arming the Muslims was the only way of making the whole situation stable. It was the West's dithering that made the Balkans unstable and gave Milosevic the opportunity to carry out his ethnic cleansing."

"Who said she was emotional?"

"Malcolm Rifkind, then Defence Secretary, said that she was talking 'emotional nonsense' and the American Secretary of State Warren Christopher said that her call to arm the Muslims was 'an emotional response to an emotional problem'. But only somebody who is completely inhuman could contemplate a holocaust without emotion."

Seeing how completely fixed he was in his view, and knowing

how tenacious he could be in any discussion, there seemed no point in arguing with him, especially at this hour. So I tried to steer the conversation away from the Balkan towards the United Nations and the European Union. I was interested in what he thought about the prospects of Poland and the other new Eastern European countries joining the EU, bearing in mind Thatcher's antagonism towards Europe. The answers that he gave to my questions were so comprehensive they could well have stood for Thatcher's own views now. More than an hour passed, and I took mental notes, wondering if I could palm them off in a seminar as words that the Iron Lady had imparted exclusively to me herself. He sounded so much like a mouthpiece for the woman we had once mutually loathed.

Finally, with sleep hanging heavily over me and the Champagne bottle dry, I asked him about the stalking case that had brought him before the British courts. His eyes softened and became moist. It was as if I had asked him not about a shameful crime, but about his proudest moment.

"You should have seen her here that weekend. Then you would understand. It was a revelation. I saw her arrive in the lobby. She was glowing. Then I watched her at the opening ceremony with Rocco Forte and all the other bigwigs, and afterwards at a luncheon, where she gave a small speech. I wasn't invited, but I slipped in to listen. She was mesmeric. You could have heard a pin drop. I even went to the Catholic Church in the square on Sunday morning where she attended a service. Every nook and cranny was packed. Babies were held up to see her. People wanted to touch her. She stood in front of the altar and children lined up to present her with bouquets. The priest said so many kind things about her, about how during the darkest days of communism the people of Poland had come to identify with her recognisable voice of truth and freedom and hope, that I almost thought I saw a halo, a heavenly glow."

Why I did not laugh out loud at this point I am not sure, except that madmen are irrational, and irrational behaviour always contains the possibility of the unknown, of forces that cannot be dealt with by any reasonable means, even of violence.

"The Blessed Margaret." He suddenly beamed. "Wonderful woman." He drained his Champagne and stood up, put our empty glasses on the trolley and smiled wistfully. "Now I must get on. I still have a lot of work to do." And with a brief bow he left the room.

That night I barely slept. The next morning I left for the airport an hour earlier than necessary, half expecting to see Matt appear in the foyer in a twin-set and pearls. At the reception desk there was a parcel for me. I recognised the writing on the label right away. It felt like a book, and in my haste to leave I simply zipped it into my case.

On the flight home, I had time to reflect. All I could presume was that Matt had suffered some kind of breakdown at the same time that Lady Thatcher, a woman he had been obsessed with for most of his life, had arrived in Poland. Perhaps it was induced by the holocaust commemorations; some of his distant relations, I remember him once telling me, had perished in the camps. Mixed in with this was Lady Thatcher's concern for a new holocaust in Kosovo. She was at the end of a high-octane week in the public glare for the first time in many months and she must have arrived at the hotel visibly charged. A friend of Lord Forte, she had been in and around the hotel for three day, giving Press conferences, having lunches, making speeches, happy to be in the limelight again. In the flesh, she must have appeared in a new light to Matt, and I can only assume that his passionate hatred of her had simply flipped into complete reverse, and he had become so fixated by her that, back in London, he began to follow her around. After his trial and banning order, the next best thing must have been to come back to the place where it all began, taking a position, any position in the hotel where the affair was ignited, so that every day he could be reminded of his encounter with the woman he had once so vehemently scorned, and whom he now worshipped.

His parcel turned out to be LadyThatcher's second volume of memoirs, *The Downing Street Years*, which of course ended in her mass stabbing. But that was not how the book could be allowed to close. Her story had to finish on a high note, a note of personal and public triumph. This was the moment described in the Epilogue, beside which Matt had slipped a postcard of the Hotel Bristol.

The final chapter of her life story began, "*In April 1993 I visited Warsaw as a guest of honour at the reopening of the historic Bristol Hotel. It was, in its way, a significant occasion. The Bristol had been one of the great hotels of Europe…*" She went on to recall her hero's welcome in those three elated days in Warsaw and it sounded much as Matt had described it. Feted, admired, she was clearly in her element in Eastern Europe freed at last from the tyranny of communism and safely returned to capitalism's claw. The chapter read as if her visit to the Warsaw Bristol was the climax of her career.

I read it through twice, imagining Matt hovering in the shadow of the Iron Lady's show-stopping tour. There was nothing written on the back of the postcard, but there was an inscription on the title page of the book, in blue ink:

"*To Tom Cotton, a good listener and a sound advisor*

 Best wishes,

  – *Margaret Thatcher, Warsaw*

I stared at it. Matt really had flipped. Traditionally, Napoleon was the popular persona for the insane to adopt; other world leader were obviously not far behind. On the other hand, plucking opportunity from tragedy, I began to wonder what would happen if people got to hear about this tribute from the Blessed Margaret to me. If I trotted out Matt's theories about the state of the European Union, and how to put the world to rights, who could not be impressed if I prefaced them with "*…as Mrs Thatcher said to me when I was in Warsaw…*"

I had the written evidence to prove how well she regarded me. It could do business no harm. No harm at all.

6: HIGH NOON FOR THE KING'S MOLL

Hotel Bristol
Vienna, Austria
www.starwoodhotels.com

For various reasons, I have never managed to stay at the Hotel Bristol in Vienna, though I have visited Europe's "city of music" a couple of times. I know where it is, of course. It is impossible to miss the imposing building on the corner of Kärtnerring where doormen in beige coats with braided epaulettes have tipped their bowler hats to most of the rich and famous who ever came to the Austrian capital. Opened as a hotel in 1892 and expanding into the neighbouring buildings for the next fifty years, it is an elegant place, dripping with chandeliers, Regency stripes and heavy drapes. Its Ringstrassen Salons and dining rooms belong to a baroque-Louis Seize era, a style that never seems to go out of grand hotel fashion.

Though disappointed not to stay here, I did once have a hot chocolate in the wood-panelled Bristol Bar, where a piano player in a dickie bow was tinkering with Strauss. The bourgeois opera-goers drifted in before the evening's performance at the Vienna State Opera House directly opposite. They had a ready familiarity with the pianist and the rest of the staff, as well as with one another, but I have no doubt their conventions would not be easy either to live with or to learn. Not a hair was out of place, not a shoe unshone.

All the rooms in the hotel that face the Staatsoper bear the names of famous musician managers of the opera house including Karajan, Mahler and Strauss, while the sumptuous hotel suites are named after a handful of the Bristol's early 20th-century guests: Enrico Caruso, Yehudi Menuhin, Giacomo Puccini, Sergei Rachmaninoff, Artur Rubinstein, Arturo Toscanini and the

Prince of Wales. The Prince of Wales is the only suite attributed to a man who did not make music. In fact the future Edward VIII did not like music much. He once interrupted Rubinstein at a private party in London when he had heard enough, and he viewed a night at the opera as purgatory. Wales was more of a foxtrot and gypsy-violin man, happier to be tripping across the hotel ballroom than sitting in a plush box in the building opposite, listening to Kirsten Flagstad.

The Prince of Wales is undoubtedly the king of suites, the largest in Austria and a zenith of style, and this haven of luxury may well be the greatest material legacy of the man and his lover, Wallis Simpson, who were to be drummed into permanent exile as the Duke and Duchess of Windsor. Comprising an antechamber, a double bedroom, library, dining room, office, private fitness room and sauna, it costs around four thousand euros a night, depending on the season. The suite occupies the entire floor that the Prince of Wales hired for his first visit with Wallis in February 1935 and again, after the death of his father George V, as uncrowned King Edward VIII in 1936 at the turning point in their courtship.

Hotels can be deliciously illicit places, neutral territory filled with hints of pleasure and desire. But hotels as grand as the Bristol are far too theatrical for a brief encounter. This is the stage to act out the full drama of a life-changing romance. And of course there was nothing discreet or passing about the drama of Wallis and Wales.

By early 1935 half London knew of the affair, no thanks to the Press, since the media barons had agreed on a conspiracy of silence. The Prince, heir to the throne, went on his first trip abroad with Wallis Simpson in February that year. She was among the royal party that he joined in Paris, where they boarded the Orient Express, first stopping at Kitzbuhl for a week of fun in the snow. Austria was then a favourite destination for British tourists, and there was more English to be heard on the slopes than any other foreign language.

With his party commanding fifty pieces of luggage, with his pale blue eyes and "buttercup yellow" hair, Wales and his entourage were as impossible to ignore as his grandfather and namesake had been when he travelled to Biarritz with his mistress in a party that filled eleven carriages of an exclusive royal train. And yet this latest Wales insisted on travelling under the name of one of his lesser titles, "The Earl of Chester". It can only have brought more attention on himself, just as the Austrian Press's plea to readers to leave the royal visitor alone ensured that people came to the Bristol for a chance of glimpsing the world's most celebrated bachelor prince, who was then aged thirty-nine.

At the time of his arrival in Vienna, the city was in political turmoil. Parliamentary democracy had been abolished, socialist protests were being suppressed and outside the Hotel Bristol demonstrators tried to get their messages across to this visiting monarch-in-waiting whom they imagined had some influence in matters of state. During his visit the Prince met the president and the chancellor and tried to persuade them to restore the Austro-Habsburg empire under Otto von Habsburg, a distant relation. Then he went on a tour of showcase housing estates.

But he was on holiday, too. Habitually late to bed, kept up by the nightlife of the city, he rose each day between 10am and 11am when he was brought a traditional English breakfast of grapefruit, tea, toast and marmalade accompanied by his favourite *Kaisersemmelen* rolls. Perhaps it was Wallis, with what gossips had described as her "Chinese tricks", who kept him so long between the Bristol's satin sheets. By all accounts it was a curious relationship. He liked to be mothered, and allowed Wallis on occasion to give him a public telling off. She always called him "sir" when in company, perhaps sometimes in private, too, though of course his real name was David. She was waspish, a wisecracker, a Becky Sharp, a fun hostess and impeccable dresser. The royal family loathed her.

Over breakfast the Prince of Wales mapped out his day, choosing a variety of suits and outfits events might require, expecting to change three or four times before bedtime. The hotel provided the royal party with two limousines so that they might enjoy some independence. The Prince shopped with Wallis, buying her jewellery, and when he went out alone he did not stop thinking about her. He was seen purchasing lingerie, and although everyone could guess whom it was for, the cabaret artists in Vienna made fun of it, pretending ignorance of Wallis and impersonating HRH in drag, wearing the lingerie himself.

As a mistress, the twice-married Bessie Wallis Warfield from Baltimore was only hinted at. She was waiting for the right moment, but both her time and her husband's money were running out. Juggling both Ernest Simpson and the Prince, who had been candid with each other about the affair, was exhausting, and she wrote to her mother to say that if the Prince did not cement their relationship soon, he might find someone younger and more suitable, in which case her lifestyle would be severely curtailed.

A year after they had returned from Vienna, Ernest Simpson, an Anglo-American businessman, attempted to join a company of masons but was turned down because "it was against Masonic law to accept cuckolds". At this point the Prince, who was himself a member of the lodge, stepped in to say that he and Wallis were simply good friends, and as a result Simpson was accepted.

By the time Mrs Simpson returned to her favourite Hotel Bristol nineteen months later, however, it was clear to the world that she was neither just a good friend of the Prince nor merely another member of the royal party. She was very definitely the king's moll.

By tradition, on the death of a monarch the royal family used to go into mourning for twelve months. When George V died on January 20 1936, the Prince of Wales automatically became Edward VIII, and a date would eventually be set for his coronation the following May. Yet little more than six months later he was openly courting a married woman deemed completely unsuitable as a consort, let alone a queen. Sailing in the face of all convention, the vehicle to be used for the courtship was the 1,391-ton Nahlin, rented from Lady Yule, the widow of a jute multi-millionaire, whose sense of patriotism had encouraged her to form British National Films with J Arthur Rank. The yacht was extensively modified to Edward's specifications, in particular the library was removed from the front of the vessel, making a spacious apartment for the monarch, while the other guests and their maids and valets bunked up in the stern. This floating hotel, with a crew that promised utmost discretion, awaited them in Sibenik on the Dalmatian coast in what is now Croatia.

This time, even more unnecessarily, Edward chose the Earl of Lancaster as the name to be written on his baggage tags. This was the title his grandfather had used when travelling incognito, when it was said that the word "Lancaster" was enough to open every royal suite across Europe. In August the king once again met Wallis and the royal party in Paris where they took up a whole carriage on the Orient Express courtesy of Benito Mussolini, the Fascist dictator of Italy. En route they stopped for tea with Prince Paul, Regent of Yugoslavia, with whom Edward had been at Oxford. In photographs with the King, Paul can be seen wearing a trilby and looking like a loss adjuster. In Corfu the couple would dine with George II of Greece and his English mistress, Joyce Britten-Jones – "the Mrs Simpson of Greece".

And so the yacht sailed, not incognito, but cheered on its way by 20,000 well-wishers on the Sibenik quayside and trailed by two British warships. The month-long voyage traced the coasts of Dalmatia, Albania and Greece, where she slipped through the Corinth Canal, her patron in nothing but shorts and deck shoes. There were crowds everywhere they went, taking photos and mobbing them any time they strolled ashore. In Dubrovnik hundreds of well-wishers followed the couple through town shouting, "Long live love!" There is many a restaurant in ports along the Adriatic and Ionian seas still dining out on their famously romantic guests, while the island of Rab likes to advertise the fact that that the couple were given municipal consent to swim naked at Kandalora, the oldest nudist beach on the Adriatic.

The king made it perfectly clear that he wanted to be seen as a modern monarch and had little appetite for formal occasions, which he did his best to avoid. Even when they finally arrived in Istanbul to a tumultuous seaborne reception, he was annoyed that, as the first British monarch ever to visit Turkey, he could not play golf, and would instead have to meet the country's leader, Mustafa Kemal, known as Atatürk. In the end the two men enjoyed each other's company and Wallis thought the founder of the modern Turkish state worth "fifty Hitlers". After laying on a seaborne "Venetian" spectacle and firework display, Atatürk lent them his gilded railway carriage to take them as far as the Bulgarian border where Czar Boris took over with a train of his own. He and Edward had boyish fun driving it. In Yugoslavia Prince Paul provided another train and a meal, but Edward was disgracefully discourteous to his host for delaying their arrival in Vienna.

He had been so looking forward to returning to the Bristol in "the city of music", because it was there, he knew, that the holiday romance would reach a climax and the relationship pass the point of no return.

"*Whatever dispiriting effects the Belgrade interruption may have had upon David's spirits were quickly dispelled by the more familiar atmosphere of Vienna,*" Wallis Simpson wrote in her autobiography. "*Here in the ancient and urbane capital on the Danube, with its long tradition of royalty and sympathy for romance, our happy summer reached its high noon.*"

They were met by Austrian dignitaries at Vienna railway station at 1pm on September 8 and after a brief exchange of greetings the king was driven to the Hotel Bristol. "*Vienna is crowded with the last visitors of the tourist season and with visitors to the Autumn Fair,*" *The Times* reported, "*but the news of his coming, and the British flag flying over the hotel, had swollen even the morning throng on the Ring, and several hundreds of Viennese and foreigners waited to give him the friendly but unobtrusive welcome which the Viennese habitually accord to the Duke of Lancaster."*

A photograph of the king stepping from the Rolls-Royce specially flown to Vienna for the occasion shows police holding back the crowd. However, the British Press was still muzzled by the agreement between Buckingham Palace and the newspaper p roprietors. *The Illustrated London News*, with a page of photographs of the king's Balkan tour, went as far as entitling their report "A Busman's Holiday", suggesting that the jaunt had been all work and no play. No such agreements existed abroad. Foreign newspapers and magazines with their paparazzi pictures of the monarch and his American mistress were seized by customs officers around Britain, while some publications would reach their subscribers with pages torn or articles cut out. Though there was no sign of Wallis in the British Press, everyone knew that she was only a heartbeat away.

In fact by the time the couple had reached Vienna, it was clear to the world that this was no holiday romance. They were back in familiar territory, on *terra firma*, and Wallis felt home and dry. Although she liked to think of Vienna in terms of candle-lit restaurants, as she came into the Hotel Bristol that day, she seemed to have weightier matters on her mind.

Elsa Maxwell, the American "hostess with the mostest", was in the lobby. "*The clicking of heels by the manager and his staff sounded like castanets and a crew of porters scurried through the door with mountains of baggage. Then the King's entourage entered, led by a small, beautifully dressed woman. Her sullen expression and the purposeful way she walked gave me the impression that she would brush aside anyone who had the temerity to get in her path.*"

The couple had six days of dedicated enjoyment at the Bristol. The shorts and deck shoes were now firmly packed away in the Duke of Lancaster's luggage and one by one the Nahlin party headed for home, leaving the couple to linger in the Austrian capital. It was time to dress up and join society again. Rudolph Paller, a hotel page boy, remembers taking the king a carnation for his button hole each day. There was golf to be played and partridge to be shot. On an outing at the Lainzer Country Club, dressed in loden cloth and a Tyrolean hat with a tuft of feathers, the king helped to bag seventy-eight birds. His new clothes included a birthday suit, which he displayed when he strolled naked into a public Turkish bath accompanied by his Scotland Yard officer and six armed Viennese policemen all completely undressed. These were the modern king's new clothes.

It was impossible to maintain a social position in Vienna without visiting the opera and Wallis insisted they went, accompanying Winifred Wagner, the composer's Hastings-born daughter-in-law and a founder of the German Nazi party, to see a full performance of *Götterdämmerung*, a favourite of the Führer. The king did not join them until the third act. He had only agreed to attend at all after Wallis told him that he could leave the box when he liked, as long as he was there when the final curtain came down. He preferred the ballet, and they both loved the Spanish Riding School.

Most of all the king liked to waltz in the ballroom of the Bristol, to dine at the hotel's restaurant, or go out to the fashionable Drei Husaren – the Three Hussars, opened three years earlier and still going today – and the Rotter Bar. He also visited an ear specialist, Professor Neuman, who had treated an ear problem the previous year. The professor pronounced that a summer of sea bathing had done him no harm. In between he kept up the "busman's holiday", touring the Vienna Fair where he visited the Indian Pavilion and lingered over exhibits of cigarette-making machines.

On his last afternoon Edward and Wallis stayed in his hotel suite and watched film footage of his visit the previous year. Then they took their leave, catching the night train and cheered on their way by thousands of well-wishers calling for their speedy return.

In Zurich, the king left Wallis and took a plane of the King's Flight back to London to face the music. When Wallis reached England she knew there was no going back and she pursued an action for divorce against Ernest Simpson, citing his own adultery. Britain had no equivalent of America's Reno, a town where anyone could receive a swift separation, and any divorce that the courts agreed on would have to wait a further six months to become absolute, and even that was not guaranteed. The couple were concerned that the case might not be settled before the coronation, when Edward now intended to have Wallis by his side.

The London divorce courts were fully booked, so alternatives were sought, finally settling on Ipswich in Norfolk, not far from the royal Sandringham estate. Even here there were delays, during which foreign correspondents, unbound by the continuing conspiracy between the British Press and Buckingham Palace, had to fill column inches of their newspapers as they awaited the hearing. Roaming the streets of the county town looking for stories, American journalists took to writing about Ipswich itself, informing their readers that this was where Thomas Wolsey, Henry VIII's powerful minister, had been born.

When the case finally went through on a nod in October 23, the Chicago *Sun-Times* was able to run the headline: KING'S MOLL RENO'D IN WOLSEY'S HOME TOWN.

The decree absolute came through six months later, and would have been just in time for the coronation. But by Christmas the king had abdicated and returned to Austria, staying with friends, where he waited until Wallis's divorce came through the following May. They immediately married in France, to become the Duke and Duchess of Windsor.

According to her own account, in her autobiography, the morning after their wedding the Duchess awoke to find the Duke standing by their bed. With his boyish smile, he asked, "And what do we do now?" Her heart sank.

It had been fun being the king and his moll for a while. Life would not be the same and they would never stay in Vienna's Hotel Bristol again.

7: LL Cool J and the Woman Who Shot Andy Warhol

The Bristol
San Diego, CA, USA
www.thebristolsandiego.com

Bristol Hotel
56 Mason Street, San Francisco, CA, USA

Bristol hotels are not all Grand Hotels like the ones that grace some of Europe's capitals. In fact they are anything anyone wants them to be. For instance, there's the non-profit-making Bristol in Tunis, set up in 1965 by the Algerian Freedom Movement, the FLN, and, according to my brother James, still a nice little place to stay. There are modern boutique hotels like the Bristol in Frankfurt, or the chic 100-room Bristol in the Gaslamp Quarter of San Diego, California, which has a Pop Art theme and genuine art works, including silk screens by Andy Warhol. And there are low-rent residential SRO (single room only) Bristols like the one in the Tenderloin district of San Francisco, where Valerie Solanas, the woman who shot Warhol, died.

Because Bristols are for every walk of life, it is no wonder that they have become hotels of the imagination, perfectly plausible places for any type of character in a book and film to inhabit. A Hotel Bristol (actually the San Francisco Hilton) was the setting for the 1972 farce *What's Up Doc?* starring Barbra Streisand and Ryan O'Neal and involving a great deal of misplaced luggage. *Hotel Bristol* is the title of novels by Canadian Michael Tremblay and by Polish writers Ewa Pustola-Kozlowska and Mary Peninska. *The Hotel Bristol* by Tri Smith is a steamy read about a Time Square hotel, with a sequel.

The world's seediest Bristol, however, must be the fantasy

establishment in New York's Jamaica, Queens, where the action in Room 615 is described on the 1987 *Bigger and Deffer* CD by LL Cool J. It was Sophie who unearthed this little gem. Sophie still went clubbing with friends long after we started our relationship though she was never a great fan of New Yorker LL Cool J ("Ladies Love Cool J"ames Todd Smith), the King of Hip Hop, partly because of the lyrics in songs like this.

"*A Bristol girl,*" raps LL Cool J, "*is one of a kind, / And if you know her good enough she won't make you stand in line...*" He describes some of the sexual activities that take place in the hotel, and in case you are any doubt where all this is happening, there is a chorus to keep reminding you: "*Room 615, The Bristol Hotel!/ Where that at? Jamaica, Queens!*" The pay-off is that clients are likely to end up in the Aids clinic having a blood transfusion. After listening to the track, I added my own contribution to the sum of human knowledge by pointing out to Sophie that in Lord Bristol's day "Bristol waters" with a little added claret or red wine was a recommended cure for virulent gonorrhoea.

James Todd Smith was born in Bay Shore, Long Island, on January 14, 1968, five months before the writer, actress, lesbian and part-time prostitute Valerie Solanas shot and wounded Andy Warhol some forty miles away at the Factory in Manhattan. She had written a play called *Up Your Ass*, which was as acceptable in polite society as LL Cool J's lyrics, though she would have had nothing good to say about the singer, even though she was something of a Bristol girl herself. She hated all men who went with prostitutes. It was nothing personal. She just wanted to eradicate the world's male population, that was all. She hated especially men whom she thought had control over her, which was most of those she met, certainly when they were buying her time, but also when she was submitting something more than her body – her writing, her creativeid. In early 1967 she gave Andy Warhol *Up Your Ass* to look at, hoping he would put it on as a play.

Valerie Solanas was the founder of S.C.U.M., the Society for Cutting Up Men, which consisted entirely of herself and an

11,000-word manifesto that she had mimeographed and was trying to sell around the city streets about this time. The first paragraph of the S.C.U.M. Manifesto is an encouragement to "*thrill seeking females... to overthrow the government, eliminate the money system, institute complete automation and destroy the male sex.*" She took no male hostages.

When Maurice Girodias, owner of Olympia Press, arrived in New York that spring, he was looking to expand his list of titles to appeal to a new generation of open-minded readers, as his father had done when he published Henry Miller and Anaïs Nin. Solanas's Manifesto was just the kind of thing that would maintain the Parisian publishing house's reputation for ground-breaking work. He met Solanas and drew up a contract for a novel based on her polemic. She used the $600 advance to see the West Coast, and she found herself in San Francisco as it was building up to the Summer of Love.

By May she was back in New York and she wanted to know what had happened to her play. Warhol had no idea. He couldn't find it. The Factory had moved from 31 East 4th Street to the 6th floor of 33 Union Square and things had gone astray. He offered her parts in films, as a strident lesbian in *I a Man* and a non-speaking role in *Bikeboy*, but she still wanted her script back, or at least proper compensation for the loss of the play.

She was also becoming convinced that the contract she had signed with Girodias meant that he would be entitled not only to everything she had written but also to anything she may ever write. She was being manipulated, controlled, dumped on first by Warhol, then by Girodias. By men. In the end this idea got to her so much that she put a .32 automatic in a brown paper bag and went to the Chelsea Hotel to find Girodias. He was away for the weekend. So she went over to the Factory and waited for Warhol to arrive. When he turned up she fired three bullets at him. Two missed, the third hit his chest, tearing through his left lung, spleen, stomach, liver and oesophagus and he went down in unbearable pain; then she fired at his friend the Canadian art critic Mario Amaya, who took a flesh wound in the hip. Finally she aimed at the forehead of Warhol's manager, Fred Hughes. The gun jammed, saving his life, and she left the building.

Solanas turned herself in and was sentenced to three years. Warhol, who had been pronounced dead on arrival at hospital, spent two months in care and was affected by the wound for the rest of his life. In fact it helped to kill him.

Olympia Press published the S.C.U.M. Manifesto shortly after the shooting, and it has never been out of print. It didn't help Solanas, who had sold the rights. After her release she continued her downward trajectory, begging, touting for trade and going in and out of mental institutions. She ended up on the West Coast where she lived in welfare hotels and spent her last years panhandling and working as a street prostitute, an activity she had pursued almost since childhood, when she had been abused by her father. There had been a latent hope that the sound of a typewriter in her room in the residential Bristol Hotel at 56 Mason Street in San Francisco's Tenderloin may have been the sound of a creative genius trying to replace the lost manuscript. But emphysema and pneumonia caught up with her and she died at the Bristol in obscurity aged fifty-two in 1988, just a year after Warhol and two years after her other victim, Mario Amaya, who succumbed to an Aids-related illness.

Like many people who have had brief fame and died in obscurity, when she was no longer in a position to raise any objections, her life's work and story was picked up, dusted off and brought back into the limelight. *I Shot Andy Warhol*, starring Lily Taylor as Solanas and Jared Harris as Warhol, came out in 1996. Meantime an archivist working on the Warhol estate finally located *Up Your Ass* at the bottom of a trunk containing lighting equipment. In 1998, on the thirtieth anniversary of the shooting, the Warhol Museum in the artist's home town of Pittsburgh included the forty-page manuscript that had ultimately cost the artist his life in an exhibition about Valerie Solanas. A visitor to the exhibition was George Coates, a radical theatre producer from

San Francisco who likes nothing more than watching taboos being broken.

"I was astonished at how offensive it still is," Coates told a local paper with evident delight. "It's a take-no-prisoners farce. It shows Valerie as an artist, as a very funny satirist."

In January 2000 Coates directed its premier a few blocks from the Bristol Hotel, at the Methodist Cathedral near San Francisco's City Hall. Billed as "Real Art Is Murder", it starred a butch dyke named Bongi Perez, played by lesbian comedian Karen Ripley, and it ended with a woman in a fur coat strangling her son. It had some humour, a lot of references to excrement, a few karaoke tunes added by Coates and a high curiosity value.

Despite the obscurity of her last years, Solanas is in no danger of being forgotten and her SCUM Manifesto continues to sell, while the well-named Factory churns out entertainment. *Factory Girl*, made in 2006, is the story of Warhol and his superstar Edie Sedgwick. Guy Pearce and Sienna Miller played the starring roles and Lady Victoria Hervey was a contender to play the part of another Warhol superstar, Baby Jane Holzer.

Lady Victoria's half brother, John Hervey, the Seventh Marquess of Bristol, knew Warhol. In the 1970s, before his arrest and imprisoned in for trafficking several million pounds' worth of heroin, he was part of the New York Britpack. Though he could give parties and was probably not ungenerous with his drugs, it is hard to know what the dissolute lord had in common with the Pop artist. Art appreciation did not run in the family. Only a fraction remains of the Earl-Bishop's extensive purchases from his European tours. A large consignment of early Renaissance paintings that were in storage in Rome were sent, without his knowledge, to Elba to escape the French, only to be lost when the ship went down. "*Pictures by Cimabué, Gotto, Guido de Siena, Marco di Siena, & all that old pedantry of paintings which seemed to show the progress of art at its resurrection,*" Bristol wrote, "*had they ever been left to the mercy of the French, might have been redeemed for a trifle, being like so many trifles, of no use to the owner.*"

But Napoleon did have use for such trifles. Another cargo of acquisitions, paintings, sculptures and antiquities collected over half a dozen years and awaiting transportation to Ickworth, were confiscated by the French, who were plundering Rome's treasures for the Louvre. Bristol never managed to retrieve "...*all that immense and valuable & beautiful property of large mosaick pavement, sumptuous chimney pieces for my new house, & pictures, statues, busts & marbles without end, first rate Titians & Raphaels, dear Guidos, and three old Caraccis – gran Dio! che tesoro...*"

Bristol's loss was our loss, too, for otherwise these would all now be on show at Ickworth. Or they may have been sold, as the family fortune dwindled, to support excessive lifestyles.

John Hervey, the drug-fuelled Seventh Marquess, contemporary and friend of Andy Warhol, the world's highest priced living artist, had no interest whatsoever in art. Nor did he ever bother to read a book. A small silk screen of a dollar bill that Warhol had given him was casually hung in his New York apartment and in idle moments he would throw darts at it.

Valerie Solanas would have approved.

8: PARIS HILTON AND LADY VICTORIA HERVEY

**Hotel Castellana Intercontinental
(formerly the Castellana Hilton)
Madrid, Spain
www.ichotelsgroup.com**

"If you had to…" James laid a tabloid paper on the low coffee table beside my laptop.

I looked across at the front page colour picture of two blonde socialites out on the town: Lady Victoria Hervey and Paris Hilton. Paris was fixing Lady V's watch, or perhaps it was a bracelet, that had come adrift. Photographed at a nightclub in dresses that clearly didn't like to stay up late, their whole evening seemed to be happily unravelling. The hotelier's granddaughter and the mitred earl's descendant embodied an idea of good times. But seeing these two heiresses partying together brought something else to mind.

I took the question back to James: "Bristols or Hiltons – if you had to?"

"Just for one night?"

"Including breakfast."

"Hilton every time. But it would have to be a Cold War classic, a glass high-rise with views all around."

James and I were in the British Airways Club Class Lounge at Heathrow's Terminal 2, trying to pass away the time that was stretching into oblivion, thanks to the knock-on effect of a lightning strike in French air traffic control that had delayed flights right across Europe. It was just coincidence that we were both there. I was waiting for a flight to Tallinn and a meeting of Baltic businessmen, and he was on his way to Helsinki for a conference on "The Dynamics of Poverty: Social Omnibus or Underclass Wagon?" I never found out what the answer to that question was.

At first, I wasn't sure if my brother's answer to my proposition was serious or if he was just being perverse. I had certainly always avoided Hiltons because I thought they were brash and American, the hotel equivalent of McDonalds, and because of James's politics and his work in the developing world I had imagined he would think the same. The closest I had come to staying in a Hilton was visiting the Windows Restaurant and Zeta Bar in the Park Lane Hilton in London and I will admit that the views are pretty spectacular. But it was also in London, in Trafalgar Square in the 1990s, where Hilton for the first time abandoned the branding of their hotels. They knew they were a symbol of the past.

"The big ones from the 1950s and Sixties, like Athens and Cairo, are fantastic." James removed his glasses, which was always a sign that a long discussion was imminent. "Brilliantly conceived, spacious rooms, wonderful views, swimming pools, bars, iced water taps in every room. Tip-top service, too. Americans can be relaxed with rich people. Europeans fuss. I'd choose a classic Hilton over a boutique hotel any day, and as for your Bristols, half of them are just Grand Hotels done up in that ghastly faux empire style and filled with weekday suits and middle-class weekenders who think they are minor royalty."

I protested that although this may be true of one or two Bristols, this was not always the case. There was such a diversity of Bristols that it was impossible to generalise. In fact on the whole they were nothing special but perhaps that's what I liked about them. They had an anonymity that did not try to define the guests' style, unlike brash, branded chains such as Hilton.

James began warming to his theme. "Hiltons changed so many cities and the way we viewed them. They were put down like marker pegs – *from this point on, the urban landscape grows*. They were the first skyscrapers to come to town, and they forced the clutter of urban planning to look to the future. With all their glass and concrete, they made cities white and light. Although they were transparently American, they owed everything to Le Corbusier."

In the discussion that followed I began to see that James may well have been right, but my own opinion remained fixed against Hiltons not for what they were but for what they stood for. Founded on a mix of American imperialism, capitalism and Christian fundamentalism, they grew out of the Cold War in the 1950s. Their founder, Conrad Hilton, viewed them as America's bulwarks in the front line against communism. Built close to the Soviet and Warsaw Pact nations, they would shine out like beacons across the enslaved lands. Of the first International Hilton, in Istanbul, he wrote, "*Here with the Iron Curtain veritably before our eyes, we found people who had fought the Russians for the past three hundred years and were entirely unafraid of them.*" As for the West Berlin Hilton, looking down on the East, it was an immovable daily reminder of the magnificence of mammon.

Conrad was an evangelist, a Billy Graham of the hospitality industry. He could not abide people who had no religion, and though he was a Catholic himself he did not mind what anyone else believed, as long as they had some kind of god. In the bedside locker of every one of his hotels was a King James Bible and a copy of his own book, *Be My Guest*, the story behind his fortune with several chapters giving advice on how to be happy and get on in life. In the last chapter, "There Is An Art To Living", he wonders "*What is this thing – success?*" And he offers his own thoughts under the headings:

Find Your Own Particular Talent
Be Big: Think Big. Act Big. Dream Big
Be Honest
Live With Enthusiasm
Don't Let Your Possessions Possess You
Don't Worry About Your Problems
Don't Cling to the Past
Look Up to People When You Can – Down to No One
Assume Your Full Share of Responsibility for the World in Which You Live
Pray Consistently and Confidently

I returned to the newspaper picture of Paris Hilton and Lady Victoria Hervey, whose father, the 6th Marquess of Bristol would undoubtedly have agreed with just a few of the American's ideas. He certainly thought, acted and dreamed big, and he lived with enthusiasm. But it is otherwise hard to think of two more different characters, one pulling himself up by the boot straps, the others dragging himself down by the necktie. While one built hotels the other was just as likely to burgle them.

Victor Frederick Cochrane Hervey, eldest son of the 5th Marquess of Bristol, was born in 1915 at Ickworth with more advantages than ever could be dreamed of by Conrad Hilton, who came into this world in an adobe house in San Antonio on Christmas Day in 1887. Hervey's brief passage through Eton was followed by an even briefer stop at the Military Academy at Sandhurst, where he was judged temperamentally unsuited to be an officer, and at the age of twenty-one was declared bankrupt. The Hervey Finance Corporation, which he had founded for adventures in the arms trade, had come unstuck with a £30,000 deal to supply the Provisional Government in Burgos at the start of the Nationalist uprising in Spain. Hervey had claimed to have been working as General Franco's agent for four months, but the £30,000 he had expected to receive as commission for arms consignments had, he said, failed to materialise.

Money from his father and the family's 32,000 acres was still coming in, of course, so that when he was arraigned on two counts of burglary in Mayfair in June 1939, the newspapers described his occupation as "independent". The burglaries were shameful affairs, committed with public school chums on people they knew in Mayfair. The first victim was Pauline Vincent Daubeny, sister of Prince Yurka Galitzine. Hervey's accomplice was George Hering, a gossip column journalist with the pen name Peter Proud, who persuaded Daubeny to visit his sister over the Easter weekend, leaving her Queen Street flat empty. With a key to the front door, Hervey, Hering and a clerk named Coop simply let themselves in and made off with ten rings, a tie pin, three brooches, two necklaces, six bracelets and a mink coat, with a total value £2,500. When Ms Daubeny returned on April 10 and found them missing, Hervey sent around a bunch of flowers with his commiserations for her loss.

A couple of days later, they robbed another female acquaintance. Hervey, Hering and Coop asked Gabrielle Burley of Seymour Place, to go out with them for the evening. After a few drinks in her flat, they all convened at the Ritz, then went on to the Grosvenor Hotel Bar, where behind her back the men concocted their plan. At one o'clock in the morning, after a meal at Quaglinos, they moved on to a dive called The Nest in Kingley Street off Regent Street. Here, as they watched a cabaret and drank their way through two further bottles of whisky, they stole from her handbag a pair of platinum and diamond dress clips, a platinum and diamond ring and a diamond wristwatch that were valued at £2,860.

Arrested a few days later, the three accused appeared at Marylebone Magistrates Court on April 18 and were remanded in custody. A fourth arrest was made, of a silversmith "fence", William Goodwin from West Kensington. It was reported that "one of the defendants" had threatened the others with a broken bottle through the throat if they "squealed", and now, in Brixton Prison, Hervey told Hering that he could expect the worst if he uttered a word against them. It was not until June 6 that they were committed for trial at the Old Bailey and Hervey was finally allowed bail, which was put up by his father.

The three-day trial, which began on Monday, July 1, excited intense public interest and society figures crowded the visitors' gallery. Hering and Coop pleaded guilty; Hervey and Goodwin not guilty. All the evidence suggested otherwise. Inspector Barry told the court, "There is no doubt that Hervey is the ring leader in this case." Passing sentence, Sir Gerald Dodson told the future Marquess of Bristol, "You have misused your talents, thrown away your opportunities given to you and you have been unfaithful to every trust you might have held."

Hervey was sentenced to three years' penal servitude, serving two, on the Isle of Wight. Goodwin, Hering and Coop received two years', eighteen months' and nine months' respectively. The stolen property was never found.

At this point one might have expected some sort of change of direction, a conversion towards a Conrad Hilton-style straight-and-narrow path, but Herveys have too often proved to be beyond redemption. When he was released, Victor Hervey wrote a series of boastful articles about himself in the *Sunday Dispatch*, calling himself "Mayfair Playboy No 1".

This light-fingered heir to Ickworth did not come into the title of 6th Marquess of Bristol until his uncle died in 1960, four years after debts had forced the sale of the bulk of the estate to the National Trust and the disposal of the large London mansion in St James's Square. The new Lord Bristol maintained a residence on the Suffolk estate, complaining that the upkeep cost him £300,000 a year. Victor may have been relatively impoverished but he revelled in his aristocratic role and, like his forebear, loved dressing up, sometimes most inappropriately. A decade later, as Chancellor of the Monarchist League, an international organisation that supported royalty everywhere, he amassed a number of new titles and decorations to add to his Ruritarian appearance, while growing more intemperate and writing pieces for the organisation's journal that were filled with capital letters, exclamation marks and bad grammar. *What is the world COMING TO!!*

In 1974, aged fifty-nine, he married for the third time. Yvonne Sutton, his secretary, was thirty years younger, and they became tax exiles in the principality of Monaco. Soon she was pregnant with Lady Victoria, the first of their three children, and there would be no shortage of displaced royals, pretenders all, to act as godparents at the christening, which was to be conducted by the Jesuit priest Alfonso de Zulueta at the Thomas More church in Chelsea.

In 1976, the year that Victor and Yvonne were starting a new family, Conrad Hilton, who had been single since divorcing the actress Zsa Zsa Gabor in 1946, also took a third wife, Mary Kelly.

He was eighty-nine and he was the world's most famous hotelier.

Imagine this previous generation of Bristols and Hiltons in that happy first year with their new wives. Conrad was evidently delighted to have Mary by his side. This robust Christian soldier with a ramrod-back, mellow voice and a whole heap of Southern charm could still bowl a woman over. The Marquess of Bristol, too, must have been in good spirits, stepping out with Yvonne, his new Marchioness, bulging with the evidence of his undiminished virility.

In Spain, following the death of General Franco, Juan Carlos had returned to reinstate the House of Bourbon on the throne. What better location for the Monarchist League's annual get-together than Madrid? Victor felt at home in Spain; his father had been in the diplomatic service in Latin America and consul in Bilbao and his own godmother was Juan Carlos's grandmother, Queen Victoria Eugenie. Various secretaries were given the task of finding a suitable venue for the Monarchist League to meet. Under normal circumstances the Marquess would not be seen dead in the brash Hilton hotel, but through a deal brokered by Don Luís de Requesens y Albania they were offered a conference centre and a dozen rooms in the Hilton at a discount that was difficult to refuse. Thus the Marquess and Marchioness of Bristol took the helicopter hop from the principality of Monte Carlo to Nice to board an Iberian airways flight for the Spanish capital.

Heading in from the other direction on a Pan-Am jumbo jet was Conrad Hilton, proud in this honeymoon year to be taking his bride back to visit the first hotel he ever built in Europe.

"This is where we really started to take off as a global player, honey," he told her. "The Spanish people are great. *Muy simpáticas. Aquí te vas a ser feliz.* You'll love it here."

She smiled and squeezed his hand, impressed as ever with the language over which, like so many things, he had such a command.

In their room on the tenth floor of the Hilton, Lady Yvonne, dressing for dinner, gazed out over the historic city that was fading in the twilight and was enchanted. She was so looking forward to the day when the child she was bearing, a child that already had within it her own blood mixed with some of the most noble blood in Britain, would begin to study languages, art history and all the other skills needed to take his or her place in European society. Lord or Lady, she professed not to mind what it would be, though seeing how Victor's sons had turned out, she rather hoped it would be a girl.

In the room behind her, Victor had finished pinning on his array of decorations and was rummaging through the drawers to see if there were any souvenirs worth acquiring. His hand alighted on the Gideon Bible, of which he already had several copies and which he knew more or less by heart. His conversion to Catholicism had followed his latest marriage, giving him a chance to become a member of Opus Dei, the ultimate club, the exclusive organisation to which General Franco himself and members of his Falangist cabinet belonged. Beneath the Bible was another book, and the proprietor's memoirs, *Be My Guest*. On the cover was an illustration of the moustachioed, thin-haired businessman, Conrad Hilton, with twinkling eyes and a winning smile, leaning forward in front of one of his sky-scraping hotels.

"I don't know what the Yank has to be so happy about," Victor said as he took it out and studied it. "None of his ghastly concrete blocks are a patch on Ickworth."

"Let's go down now," Yvonne said. "There are so many people I want to meet and I might not be able to stay up too late."

In the bar, members of the Monarchist League were starting to arrive. Some, like Lord Bristol, wore the badges of their orders, though the main gathering would not occur until the following day, when a conference room was booked for a series of talks and discussions. This was to be followed by a buffet luncheon at which glasses would be raised in a number of toasts, not least to the newly returned king of Spain.

"It's such a shame," Yvonne said to the first prince she spoke to, "that His Royal Highness King Juan Carlos himself is unable to attend. We so much wanted to congratulate him in person."

"Of course, Juan Carlos is practically family to me," Victor said to the monarchists. "But I know his diary has been crammed since the old *caudillo* died, and he is fully booked practically up to the millennium. Probably the most popular monarch in Europe. But he has sent me a message of good wishes, which I shall read out to you all tomorrow."

Victor's chest puffed beneath his dapper grey suit, a neutral background that showed to best effect his orders and medals, some of which he had designed himself. He was looking forward to a brisk trade in titles this weekend; he hadn't added a new one since he picked up the Grand Collar of the Order of Santa Agata di Paterno in San Marino more than a year ago.

Only a few of the monarchists were actually staying at the Hilton. Others were scattered round the city hotels, arriving on foot or by taxi and, in one case, a horse-drawn landau. Some were house guests of titled Spaniards to whom they were probably related, one or two sleeping on sofas. Perhaps they were all related. They certainly all knew each other, though many doubted some were actually who they claimed to be. Discussions would be had, arguments would break out. There would certainly be a fracas with the arrival of Juan Arcadio Lascaris Comneno, Grand Master of the Order of St Eugene of Trebizond and claimant to the Byzantine throne, a claim hotly denied by sane genealogists. Nevertheless, as a Knight Commander of the Order himself, Victor had no hesitation in inviting the pretender to this gala event, and as he ordered Champagne he rubbed his hands in anticipation of the commotions to come.

At this moment Conrad and Mary Hilton strolled into the bar with an entourage that consisted of the hotel manager and a few old friends. Don Luís de Requesens y Albania, to whom a handful of monarchists were indebted for their discounted rooms, stepped forward to greet him.

"Señor Hilton, may I present our president, His Excellency the Ambassador at Large of the Monarchist League, Victor, the Most Honorable the Marquess of Bristol, Earl Jermyn, and Baron

Hervey of Ickworth and Hereditary High Steward of the Liberty of Bury St Edmunds, and his wife, Yvonne, Lady Bristol."

Conrad, a modern high-rise to Victor's stately pile, looked down in surprise. "All those starbursts on your jacket, your Honorable Excellency, make you look more like Merlin than a Marquess," He shook Bristol's hand with crushing firmness. "I'm sure monarchs everywhere sleep easier in their beds knowing they can count on such colourful fellows for support."

Victor lost not a second in confirming the importance of their gathering at the hotel, implying that Conrad was lucky to have such glittering guests, and once more emphasising his close ties with the House of Bourbon. "God grants us our royal families and we must protect them from the mob," he said, and he gave the Americans a brief tour of the ribbons, medallions, sashes and orders that ensured he was the centre of attention.

"*Muy admirable*," said Conrad as the lengthy title of the last one came to an end.

"Oh, you speak Spanish, Mr Hilton." Lady Yvonne sounded surprised.

"Just a few words I picked up when I was on the road selling stuff around Texas as a young man."

"He really does speak it very well," Mary said with the loyalty of a new wife. "Do you speak any languages Mr Bristol?"

Mr Bristol! Victor smiled the smile of a man who has once again been proved right. "Only Russian," he said, and he proceeded to let off a blistering invective favoured by Cossacks, which he had learned forty years earlier. It had been taught to him by Victor Konasky, the head waiter at The Nest, who had been obliged to flee the country after the police had raided his club following the burglary trial.

"Oh my," said Mary. "I never heard real Russian before. It's rather frightening, isn't it?"

Not convinced that it was real Russian, Lady Yvonne was swift to change the subject. "We're here to show our support for Juan Carlos," she said.

"A fine, God-fearing young man," said Conrad. "If anyone can hold things together here, I'm sure he can."

"Have you met him?" Yvonne asked.

"We have a brief audience scheduled for tomorrow."

Mary Hilton smiled at Yvonne, who could not contain her surprise, wondering how a hotelier, an American who wasn't so much as a count, managed to obtain an audience with the King of Spain.

"He will be with us in spirit tomorrow – he has sent me a kind message," said Victor rapidly. And to show his own knowledge of Spanish and familiarity with Spain, said, "General Franco, El Caudillo de la Última Cruzada y de la Hispanidad, El Caudillo de la Guerra de Liberación contra el Comunismo y sus Cómplices, did wonders bringing up the king. The Generalissimo was a loyal friend of America and the West. If there was justice on this earth he would be made a saint."

"A brave man indeed." Conrad concurred. "One cannot but admire a nation that has so thoroughly defeated communism in our own twentieth century. The Western peoples owe Spain a great cultural debt for that. I was only glad we could do our bit for the country at a time when it was struggling so. That was back in 1952 just after World War Two when nobody in Europe was taking the communist threat seriously and they all turned their backs on Franco, even though he had remained neutral throughout the war. You know, it's a fact that in its first year this hotel brought in more than a million dollars in currency exchange, not to mention pounds, francs and liras. They really needed that, and I was proud to oblige."

"Franco still owes me £300,000," said Victor, adding an inconsequential nought to the original sum. "It's probably worth a few million by now, with forty years' interest."

"You don't say?"

The medals jangled on Victor's breast. "I helped to arm the Nationalists when they started out in Burgos in 'thirty-seven. But I was never paid a penny."

"Well, you sure helped the General to do the world a service, and I guess the Western world owes you a debt, too. Your rewards will be in heaven, Lord Bristol, I know it."

Later, at the end of the evening, they climbed into bed, Victor in purple silk pyjamas, Yvonne in a bulging pink nightgown.

"What a nice old man that Conrad Hilton turned out to be," said Yvonne

"That brash hotel-keeper? The man hasn't got any form." Victor turned his back on her to face the window.

"You could say he belongs to America's ruling class."

"Oh for God's sake, he's *trade*." She would never understand; she was middle class and could never be anything else. He smacked the pillow.

"But you two seem to have so much in common."

"Huh!" Victor pulled the duvet over his ears and was soon in the arms of Morpheus, chased there by his wife's last remark.

A few hours later, in the first twinkling of dawn, Victor awoke in need of the bathroom. At the large window, he pushed aside the curtain and stared down at the slumbering city safe now in the hands of the monarchy. It was a reminder of where he was and what he was supposed to be doing; looking down on the world was his God-given place in it. After he had relieved himself, as quietly as he could he went to his suitcase and slipped a hand into an inner compartment to find the barbed wire chain, his prized secret from Opus Dei. Removing the bottoms of his silk pyjamas, he bound the cruel device tight around his right thigh, which was already bruised and scarred. As usual it was exquisitely painful, wounding and wonderful. Just like the suffering of Jesus, it b rought him closer to the sublime agony and ecstasy of martyrdom. Tomorrow he would limp a little, to show his own infinitesimal contribution to the wounds suffered by Christ.

Dear God, he prayed, *Bless every monarch in this world and send all liberals and socialists to hell.*

Then he took a wad of lavatory paper to put between thigh

and bedsheet, to mop up any sanguine drops: *this is my blood which is shed for you...* Yvonne would be spilling blood soon. There would be another aristocrat in the world, another Bristol to mingle among the royal courts of Europe. He could not get back to sleep. He thought of his delicious pain and the speech he would be giving in a few hours' time, reasserting the divine right of kings. But Yvonne's last words kept coming into his head, repeating themselves like a mantra. "*So much in common with Conrad, with common Conrad...*"

Beside him, she and the baby-to-be were lost to the world. He sighed, sat up and switched on the light, bracing his tormented right leg. Then he reached into the cupboard beside the bed and pulled out *Be My Guest*, which he started to read from page one.

Somewhere among these thousands of words he hoped to find what on earth it was that he had in common with one of the most successful businessmen on the planet.

9: LEON TROTSKY AND THE PHANTOM HOTEL BRISTOL

Hotel Bristol
Plaza Nacaxa 17, Mexico City, Mexico
Tel: +52 5336060

It was my brother James who brought the curious case of Trotsky and the phantom Hotel Bristol to my attention. The incident was, he said, a reminder that any fraudster or philanderer looking for an alibi should not instantly answer "the Bristol" when called to account over what hotel he or she was staying in, for although hotels called Bristol may seem to be everywhere, there are one or two places where they do not exist.

James had been in Mexico City on some junket and even though he had treacherously failed to stay at the city's Hotel Bristol – by all reports a moderately priced, 140-room, centrally located hotel in the Zona Rosa near the British and US embassies, used by Mexican businessmen but with a family-run air – he more than made up for it by bringing to my attention a Hotel Bristol that played a crucial role in the life of Leon Trotsky. James is not a great art connoisseur but he has always been interested in Freda Kahlo, and part of his visit was to see the artist's famous Blue House in the rural suburb of Coyoacán, where she had lived with her husband Diego Rivera. It was Rivera who has helped to secure asylum in Mexico for Trotsky, who stayed in the house on his arrival in 1936 and briefly had an affair with Kahlo.

Lenin's death in 1924 meant that either Trotsky or Josef Stalin, the other two instigators of the October Revolution, would become the Soviet leader. Stalin came to power and Trotsky, together with his wife Natalia and son Leon Sedova, was expelled from the party and sent into exile, first to Istanbul, then France and Norway, before being granted a safe haven in Mexico.

Although out of sight, Trotsky was never far from Stalin's murderous mind and the Soviet leader continued to discredit Trotsky and plot his assassination. He also systematically began ridding the Soviet Union of every leading communist in the Great Purge and Terror that culminated in the Moscow Trials, which began not long before the time of Trotsky's arrival in Mexico. Stalin himself was the only surviving member of Lenin's Politburo not arraigned at the trials. Close associates and members of his own family were killed, every important survivor of the October Revolution, every heroic militant and worthy party worker was done away with, and almost half of the 75,000 officers of the Red Army, which Trotsky had founded, were arrested or shot. The number of victims ran into millions.

Under torture and threats, thousands confessed to crimes that had never taken place. The trials shocked the world and split the communist party abroad, not least in Spain where civil war was getting under way. Trotsky became a hot potato no government wanted to touch. The Norwegians kept him under virtual house arrest and when Stalin applied economic pressure, threatening to renegue on the purchase of the Norwegian herring catch, they threw him out. No Western country would have him. But in Mexico, home of the 20th century's first revolutionary government, Diego Rivera persuaded president Lazaro Cárdenas to take him in.

So on December 19, 1936, Leon and Natalia set sail on Ruth, a Norwegian tanker, for Mexico. Disarmed, guarded and forbidden from communicating with the rest of the world, the couple were at sea through the new year, arriving at the port of Tampico twenty-one days later, on January 9. Afraid for his life, Trotsky refused to step ashore until he had been met by his hosts. A small crowd was on the quayside to greet them and eventually he emerged, dressed in tweeds and plus fours with a white cap and carrying a briefcase and cane. The Mexican president was represented by General Beltrán, and Diego Rivera, sick with kidney trouble and furious that he was unable to attend, was represented by Frida Kahlo.

The party boarded the president's train, the Hidalgo, and they all got on well. "*Having escaped a sickening atmosphere and a state of exhausting uncertainty, we found everywhere nothing but kind concern and hospitality,*" Trotsky wrote. Formality was broken with song, the presidential guard giving hearty renditions of heroic tunes from the Zapata revolution, Americans sang *Joe Hill*, and Frida Kahlo added Mexican folk ballads.

Two days later they arrived in Coyoacán, then a leafy village, today a pleasant corner of the world's largest city. Rivera, recovered more or less to his robust self, was there to meet them and he and Trotsky became instant comrades. Natalia, relieved at last to have found a place of rest, later recalled, "*It was a low, blue house, with a patio filled with plants, cool rooms, collections of pre-columbian art and countless paintings.*"

The house had been built by Guillermo Khalo three years before the birth of his favourite daughter. The photographer had vacated the house he still lived in with Frida and Diego, as well as his other daughter, Cristina, for their special guests. He had no idea who Trotsky was and when told what he did for a living handed on the advice that if a man wanted to get on, he should stay out of politics. That first night Rivera, ever the man of drama and action, returned to his nearby home in San Angel to fetch a Thompson machine gun and join two other gun-toting Mexicans to stand guard at the house.

Meantime the Moscow Trials had continued to hog the world's headlines. Throughout the trials, Trotsky's name came up many times, accused with a whole bag full of heinous crimes against the Soviet Union – including being a member of British intelligence and an agent of Hitler and the Japanese Emperor – committed over a number of years. But it was not until the Zinovievite-Trotskyite trial in August that the case against Trotsky and his son Leon Sedov had been heard, and he had been found guilty on all counts.

In the United States, the American Committee for the Defense of Leon Trotsky attracted many left-wing figures. It was imperative, they believed, to show the world that these allegations were entirely false and that the trials were a charade. As a result, an independent Commission of Inquiry was set up, to be held at the Blue House in Coyoacán. Dr John Dewey, a respected Professor Emeritus of Philosophy at Columbia University in New York, then 78 years old and not in the greatest of physical health, was persuaded to take the chair. Taking the express train from New York, he joined Carleton Beals, an American journalist, Otto Rühle, a founder of the German Communist Workers Party and a former member of the Reichstag, Benjamin Stolberg, the American labour writer, and Suzanne La Follette, the American author and editor of *The New Freeman*, who acted as secretary. Albert Goldman, a Chicago lawyer, represented Trotsky and Albert M. Glotzer, a court reporter from Chicago, recorded the evidence during the week-long proceedings that began on April 10, 1937.

Sessions were held in the largest room in the Blue House, which for the duration was protected by brick and sandbag barricades six feet high. A long table was set up for Trotsky, Natalia and the commission, and forty seats were provided for journalists and guests. It was an excuse to dress up, a chance to catch the public eye. Rivera arrived in a broad-brimmed hat decorated with peacock feathers. Frida, in Indian costume and heavy ethnic jewellery, kept close to the accused. (Trotsky was not averse to flirtation, though he had little time for subtlety and generally went straight for the knee beneath the table. An attempt to ensnare Frida's sister, Cristina, who lived next door, was more elaborate; for this, *El Viejo* – the Old Man, as Frida called him – arranged an emergency fire practice that would end with his escape into her house.)

In spite of all the other accusations, the actual case that was produced against Trotsky in Moscow had rested on the evidence of a single week in November 1932 when Trotsky had been invited to give a lecture on the Russian Revolution to the Danish Social Democratic Student Organisation. An eight-day visa had allowed him to travel to Denmark from Istanbul. Evidence was given by three defendants in the trial, Eduard Holtzman, Konan

Berman-Yurin and Fritz David, who claimed that they had visited Copenhagen to meet Trotsky and his son Sedov, and Trotsky had instructed them to commit various terrorist acts against leading figures in the Soviet Union.

In his opening statement at the Blue House, Albert Goldman brought up the crucial matter of the Hotel Bristol.

"Our evidence will show that Leon Trotsky never met and never heard of Berman-Yurin or Fritz David, that the said Berman-Yurin and Fritz David never met Leon Trotsky at Copenhagen or anywhere else, and that Trotsky never had any correspondence with them. Holtzman, the most important of the three witnesses who claimed to have visited Trotsky in Copenhagen, testified that he met Trotsky's son in the vestibule of the Hotel Bristol and that from there he was brought by Sedov to Trotsky's apartment. We shall show by written and oral testimony that Trotsky's son, at the time in question, was not in Copenhagen but in Berlin, and that Trotsky and his wife, Natalia, were able to see their son only in France, on the train returning from Denmark. We shall prove that Sedov made several efforts to reach Copenhagen, but without any success."

The Hotel Bristol in Copenhagen was the key point in Trotsky's defence, as it became clear on the third day of the hearing.

GOLDMAN: On the question of the Hotel Bristol, on page two of the official report of Court Proceedings, published by the People's Commissariat of Justice of the USSR, dealing with the question of the Trotskyite-Zinovievite terrorist centre, Holtzman testifies and says: "I agreed, but I told him that we could not go together, for reasons of secrecy. I arranged with Sedov to be in Copenhagen within two or three days, to put up at the Hotel Bristol and meet him there. I went to the hotel straight from the station, and in the lounge met Sedov."

Now, he says here – and we want to call the Commissioners' attention to that fact – in testifying as to what the arrangements were in Berlin, that he arranged with Sedov to meet him in Copenhagen at the Hotel Bristol. The inference would be that he knew in Berlin that there was a Hotel Bristol in Copenhagen, and made arrangements to meet there. Now, immediately after the trial and during the trial, when the statement, which the Commissioners can check up on, was made by him, a report came from the Social-Democratic Press in Denmark that there was no such hotel as the Hotel Bristol in Copenhagen; that there was at one time a hotel by the name of Hotel Bristol, but that was burned down in 1917. The guide "Baedeker" of 1917 includes the name of Hotel Bristol. That was the report of the Social-Democratic Press of Denmark, which went the rounds throughout the world Press. About five or six months thereafter, the Communist Press issued a statement to the effect that whereas there was no Hotel Bristol, right next to Hotel Bristol Café…

DEWEY: Next to the Hotel Bristol?

GOLDMAN: Pardon me. Whereas there was no Hotel Bristol, there was a hotel by the name of Grand, and right next to the Grand Hotel there was a café called the Bristol Café. The photograph appears in a magazine *Soviet Russia Today*, of March, 1937. The magazine is the official organ of the Friends of the Soviet Union, if I am not mistaken. At any rate, the Commission can look through the magazine and satisfy itself that it is very, very hostile to Trotsky and exceedingly friendly to the Stalin Government in the Soviet Union. This photograph, which I now hand to the Commission, is a photograph allegedly showing that there is some connection with the name Bristol and the word "hotel". I show you this photograph, a radio photograph especially cabled for by *Soviet Russia Today* and received from Nord Press of Denmark through the Radio Corporation of America on February 22nd. I show the photograph to the Commissioners and ask them to examine this photograph first. I also show the Commissioners a sketch purporting to show the exact location of the Grand Hotel and the Café Bristol. This sketch is from the magazine called *Rundschau*, a German magazine which is also very friendly…

TROTSKY: It is a publication of the Comintern and it is in German.

GOLDMAN: After *Inprecorr* ceased publication, the *Rundschau* took its place as the official organ of the Comintern.

TROTSKY: *Rundschau* is published in Switzerland.

GOLDMAN: This sketch allegedly shows the connection between the Grand Hotel and the Café Bristol, showing that the Bristol Café is supposed to be right next to the Grand Hotel, and, if I am not mistaken, with an entrance leading from the hotel, the Grand Hotel, directly into the Café Bristol.

TROTSKY: Not an entrance, if you permit me. It is a cross…

STOLBERG: It looks like a door there.

TROTSKY: I am not sure.

GOLDMAN: Let the Commissioners investigate for themselves. Mr Rühle reads German, and can tell the Commissioners exactly what this is supposed to identify.

LA FOLLETTE: This is Scandinavian.

STOLBERG: The story is in German.

(*Attorney Goldman hands document to the Commission.*)

GOLDMAN: The Commissioners will see that the photograph published in *Soviet Russia Today* has the word "Hotel". The word "Grand" does not appear on the photograph. At least, I cannot make it out. Whether it is cut off, or whether actually the fact is that it is not there, I am unable to state from an observation of the photograph itself. The word "Bristol" appearing on the extreme right of the photograph appears in very clear letters, and the word "Konditori" appearing to the left of the word "Bristol" is hardly visible, although it is visible. I mention this fact to indicate that evidently the photograph was touched up for the purpose of indicating that there is such a hotel as Hotel Bristol. Will the Press take a look at that?

Now, I have an affidavit of B. J. Field and Esther Field, who are in New York and subject to be cross-examined by the full Commission after this preliminary Commission, or by another sub-commission, and in this affidavit B. J. Field and Esther Field make the following statement. Referring to the photo in *Soviet Russia Today*, they say:

"*Directly next to the entrance to the hotel, and what appears as a big black splotch in the photo, is actually the location of the Café next to the Grand Hotel and it is not the Konditori Bristol! The Konditori Bristol is not next door, but actually several doors away, at quite a distance from the hotel, and was not a part of it in any way, and there was no door connecting the Konditori ('candy store' it would be called here) and the Grand Hotel! Although there was such an entrance to the café which is blackened out in the photo, and which was not the Bristol.*"

In other words, between the Grand Hotel and the Konditori Bristol there was a café and between the hotel and the café there was an entrance, but there was no entrance at all connecting the hotel and the Bristol Konditori. B. J. Field and Esther Field were actually in that café and they were also in the hotel, so they are speaking from personal knowledge. They say further:

"*As a matter of fact, we bought some candy once at the Konditori Bristol, and we can state definitely that it had no vestibule, lobby, or lounge in common with the Grand Hotel or any hotel, and it could not have been mistaken for a hotel in any way, and entrance to the hotel could not be obtained through it. At the time of this trip to Copenhagen. we knew of no Danish Trotskyites and we do not believe*" – Here I want to emphasise the statement that in the Communist Press the statement was made that the Café Bristol was the "hang out" for Danish Trotskyites – "*At the time of this trip to Copenhagen, we knew of no Danish Trotskyites, and we do not believe that there were any.*" One of the German comrades, in spite of the language barrier, was sent to the headquarters of the Copenhagen Stalinists to invite them to Trotsky's lecture.

I think we have proved, on the basis of all the documents, first, that Sedov was never in Copenhagen, and second, there was no such hotel as Hotel Bristol where Holtzman claims that he allegedly met Sedov in Copenhagen.

The proof seemed conclusive. The commission returned to New York for the full enquiry, which in December exonerated Trotsky and Sedov of all accusations.

Trotsky enjoyed a brief summer of love with Frida Kahlo, before falling out with Rivera and quitting the Blue House. He and Nathalia afterwards set up home in a crumbling bourgeois folly in nearby Calle Viena, which they fortified.

That summer, leaders of the Trotskyite POUM in Republican Spain were arrested. A photograph taken the previous year shows a woman in a siren-suit uniform, her right fist held high, on the streets of Barcelona at the head of a pro-Stalin PSUC militia. Her name is Caridad Mercader. Four years later her son Jaime Ramón Mercader del Rio Hernandez, who had gained the confidence in the Coyoacán household, dug an ice pick deep into Trotsky's skull as he sat at his desk. Hospitalised, *El Viejo* was operated on, went into a coma and died the following night.

Mercader survived a beating from Trotsky's guards, but it was some time before his real identity was known. Even then, he refused to speak. In fact he had been brought into the NKVD, Stalin's secret police, through his mother's lover Leonid Eitingon. After a trial, he served twenty years in Mexico's prisons. In 1956 Nikita Kruschev denounced the Moscow Trials and his predecessor's regime of "suspicion, fear and terror" in a speech to the 20th Congress of the Communist Party. Released from jail four years later, Mercador returned to the Eastern bloc where he was given the Order of Lenin and a place of honour in the KGB Museum. He died in Havana in 1978.

But what of Tolstoy's accusers, Eduard Holtzman, Konan Berman-Yurin and Fritz David, three of the sixteen defendants in the First Moscow Trial in 1936? They had not connived with Trotsky, so why did they say that they had, knowing that they themselves would be sentenced to death for their "confessions"?

James said that it was obvious that either they had been tortured, or their families had been threatened. They would die anyway, but because of their confessions they thought their families would be safe.

"If anyone ever threatened to harm Kate or the children," he said, "I'd do whatever they asked."

I didn't say anything. It seemed to me like another good reason for not having children.

10: GAMBLING WITH MARADONA

Casino Central
Playa Bristol, Mar del Plata, Argentina
www.mardelplatawebcam.com.ar

"Smoking kills," James always used to say.

He had never liked the smell of tobacco. When he was eight he ran off to stay with our grandmother, who relayed the message home that he would not return until my father had stopped smoking because it was going to kill him and he obviously didn't love us if he was going to turn us into orphans. It did the trick. It certainly worked better than the notices on the windows of the Express from Buenos Aires to the Riviera on that first day in November, 2005. My brother claimed that they were clearly labelled: "Prohibido fumar". So when a cloud of cigar smoke passed by in the corridor, he didn't hesitate to point out the dangers of the habit, even though the *fumador* was Argentina's most famous son.

Diego Maradona looked round. "Eh?"

"Cigars especially." James has a knack of being able to be blunt and engaging at the same time. Perhaps it is the twinkle that sits in the corner of his eyes; perhaps it is the inflection in his voice; perhaps it is the fact that his face is wide open, and a smile never seems far away. Whatever it is, he meets people effortlessly. Maradona raised the cigar high above his head and explained that it was a gift from Fidel Castro, the way he might have said that it was a gift from God.

James stood his ground. "Fidel can afford to give them away," he said. "He doesn't want them any more. His doctors have banned him from smoking and he has even brought in no-smoking laws. He knows cigars are fatal."

Maradona wetted his eager lips on the chocolate-coloured

torpedo. "*Hombre*," he said (all Spanish speakers say *hombre* when James relates a tale; he is a good mimic). "*Hombre*, all life is fatal. And do me a favour, don't listen to those stories. The media makes them up. Fidel and El Diego, they don't die so easy. Besides, only British and Yanky *capitalistas* get upset about such things. They worry they will catch something from the thighs of the mulatto *chicas* where these little babies are rolled into life. Me? I am happy to catch anything the *chicas* want to give me. I take that aroma down to the last *militimetro*, make sure it gets right into the marrow of my bones." The footballer grinned, thumped his barrel chest and blew smoke into James's face.

My brother, to his credit, inhaled it, held it, then blew it right back. "The marrow of your bones must be full of shit," he said.

"Fuck you, you self-righteous prick!" Maradona laughed and put an arm around him, though he had to reach up. "You health priests are beyond belief. You always think you know everything. Well, *hombre*, there are many truths about the world – Buenos Aires is the capital of Argentina; the earth goes around the sun; President Bush is a pile of *mierda* – but there are no truths about the human body. It is the greatest mystery of life. Here…" He put a hand in his pocket and took a ticket from a wad, asked James for a pen and wrote a name and number on the back.

"For your problem," he said as he handed it to James.

"What problem?"

"You have a problem with smoking. This is a good psychiatrist in Buenos Aires. The best. Call him. He will cure you. He has cured me. I have no problem with smoking. It doesn't bother me at all. Also," he pointed at the ticket, "you must come and see my television show. It will help you to see the important things in life, the pleasures and the sorrows that our bodies bring us."

Well, that's the way James tells the story of how he came to be in the audience on Diego Maradona's television show, *La Noche del Diez*, praising tobacco and accusing health organisations as being lackies of Western capitalists intent on destroying the livelihood of growers in the developing world, and depriving the working people of simple pleasure. But what James was doing on board the train taking 160 protesting leaders on this special express from Buenos Aires to Mar del Plata in the first place, I never really knew. It had been an accident, he said. He was merely going along to the Fourth Summit of the Americas as an observer for one of the charities he worked for, and when he booked a ticket from Buenos Aires, they gave him a seat on this train. His mere presence must have made Maradona think he was on the side of the flying *piquiteros*.

The idea of a carriages full of dissidents reminded me of Trotsky's journey when he arrived in Mexico sixty years earlier, and I wondered if there had been many rousing revolutionary songs.

"If only there had been," James said. "There were several well known musicians in the party but all I heard coming from Diego's VIP carriage was *Don't Cry for me, Argentina*. He may be Mozart on the pitch, but off it he's a really sick canary."

November is the traditional Spring Week in Argentina, when *porteños*, the people of Buenos Aires, head for Mar del Plata, capital of the Riviera, 400 kilometres away. But this was a special train. Its passengers included the cream of Latin American intelligentsia, cultural icons and political leaders, including Bolivia's soon-to-be prime minister, Evo Morales, and the Venezuelan prime minister, Hugo Chávez, who a couple of days earlier had organised a mock invasion of his own country to prepare his people for an American attack. The US government was the enemy. Even Daniel Katz, the mayor of the host town of Mar del Plata, had described George Bush as "the most unpleasant guy in the world" and attempts had been made to obtain a court order barring the West's most powerful politician from entering the country.

The protest that Maradona and Chávez were leading, and the general high feelings about the Summit in which the US wanted to pursue the idea of a free trade area across the Americas, had persuaded the Argentinian authorities to wrap eight miles of fencing around 250 Mar del Plata city blocks and to recruit 8,000 security guards for their protection. Military personnel in dark glasses on quad bikes patrolled the beaches and naval boats close to the shore made the marina's gin palaces look like toy yachts. Thirty-four heads of state were about to descend on the resort. A couple of days after the Maradona-Chávez protest, Bush arrived. Dead on time on Thursday afternoon Air Force One landed at Mar del Plata airport, along with its shadowing fighter planes and four Advance Warning Air Craft that would continue to monitor the skies. There were 2,000 in Bush's entourage, most already in place on the ground, which was good news for the hotel business. The president himself stayed at the Sheraton, and most of talks over the following two days took place at the five-star sea-front Hermitage Hotel.

James stayed at the 736-room Bristol Condominios Apart Hotel, another modern slab a few minutes from the Bristol Beach. The name Bristol is synonymous with Mar del Plata not for the modern condominium nor for the Bristol Beach, but because it was the name of the city's first hotel, which helped to make the resort famous. Once upon a time the Bristol Hotel here was simply the "Queen of the Riviera", the most glamorous address in all of South America.

Mar del Plata was Argentina's first resort, a fishing village like so many others around the world until the railways came. It was where *porteños* first discovered the hedonistic joys of the seaside. And they so wanted to get away. In *Far Away and Long Ago* W. H. Hudson describes Buenos Aires at about the time of the first railways. It was a cow town where the smell of blood gagged the air some distance before you reached it. Cattle were so two-a-penny that their meat was almost worthless; all they were good for was their hides. So the animals were driven to the capital, and on the outskirts they were slaughtered and skinned in the open air, their leather whisked off to the tanners, the sanguine carcases left to flies and raptors in a spreading black ocean of blood.

When the railways arrived, tracks were swiftly laid straight south towards the Atlantic coast and Mar del Plata, "straight" being the operative word because Argentina is very flat. Within two years of the first passengers' arrival the Bristol, the biggest and best hotel, opened its doors, and anyone who was anyone from "the Paris of the south" climbed aboard for the eight-and-a-half-hour journey for the season, which lasted from the November Spring Week through to March.

By the early years of the 20th century things were in full swing – though the tango was waiting to be invented and its best known composer, Astor Piazzolla, who is also Mar del Plata's most famous son, was not yet born. Argentina supported a vibrant, cosmopolitan society then, and there was some international mobility, a kind of transhumance, of all the social orders. Women went to Paris for their dresses; Italian peasants could spend a single season as waiters and return to Europe with their savings to buy land and even factories. There is no better evocation of the Hotel Bristol's Edwardian high times than this contemporary account taken from a book by W.H. Koebel called *Modern Argentina: the El Dorado of To-Day*, published in 1907.

Mar del Plata is deserving of a chapter to itself if for no other reason than that the town constitutes the sole sea-side resort of which Argentina can boast. But if it be a ewe lamb of watering places, it is, at all events, a healthy enough specimen of a progressive pleasure town. To Argentine ears the name comes with a very pleasant ring. Indeed, these latter make the most of the spot and it must be admitted that this town by the waves, in return, makes all that it can out of its visitors. Mar del Plata is fashionable to a degree, and, as such, is a costly though an agreeable place to frequent.

The words of an Argentine writer may serve as a preliminary introduction to the spot. The translation is literal, although I have taken the liberty of rendering some of the adjectives in a somewhat less flowery form than they assumed in the original. Even then it must be admitted that the composition does not err on the side of restraint. The description is the following:—

"All at Mar del Plata suggests the refinement of a bathing resort. The waves of the Atlantic beat softly on the sandy beaches. The magnificent hotels are filled with a *monde*, cultured and sociable, that fills the summer evening with joy. The English cottages and the luxurious chalets are dotted upon the slopes with all their graceful architecture and modern comfort. The days are balmy and the nights perfumed; the concerts, dances, strolls upon the 'Rambla', the gracious life of the elite – all this enlivens the spot, and causes the summer months to pass by in an enchanting fashion. And, above all, the inevitable flirtation is wont to insinuate itself in the midst of this delightful frame of mind, commencing with discreet love-making in the romantic light of the moon, in improvised excursions, during which one may enjoy with a full pulse the beauty of nature, and ending in the interchange of marriage vows to the accompaniment of delicious blushes on the part of the maiden, and nervous agitation on that of the future Benedict."

Such is Mar del Plata! Judging from this somewhat effervescent sketch, one gathers that it is in the possession of qualities which savour of various places – of Paradise, Monte Carlo, Ostend, and Margate. As a matter of fact, it is wont to be likened to Brighton by the English; a comparison that is facile rather than accurate.

The "Rambla" is essentially "dressy". The men are wont to turn out in London-built clothes of faultless cut, although in the matter of yachting caps and similar adornments the taste displayed is of a more exotic kind than would be permitted at a similar resort in England. As to the ladies, Mar del Plats is to them a veritable sun that causes costumes to break out in fresh hues every day. A festal occasion in Buenos Aires affords a revelation of what these ladies are capable of in this respect. But for a season in Mar del Plata it is no exaggeration to say that the costumier's establishments in far away Paris are ransacked. The stories told upon the point are innumerable. There are some, it is whispered – but not in too lowly a key – of these favoured millionairesses who will consent to wear no single garment twice – at Mar del Plata. There are even tales of the passionate grief that ensued when the delays in the forwarding of fresh costumes made such a contretemps possible.

The town is essentially a pleasure resort. Like every other place of the kind, it exists purely for its season, which in this case endures for about three months. The principle amusements provided for the male visitors consist of pigeon shooting, golf, and sea bathing. Beyond this there is the attraction that the Casino provides with its roulette and *petits chevaux*. This, as a matter of fact, forms one of the most important features of the spot, and a large proportion of the visitors frequent the place for no other purpose than to tempt the goddess of chance.

Sea bathing, although extremely pleasant, is an amusement in which it is necessary to indulge with the utmost caution. The surf itself, though it can thunder pretty effectually at times, is comparatively innocuous. With the ocean currents, however, the matter is very different. There are times when these run with sufficient swiftness to resist the efforts of the strongest swimmer. Indeed, for any but those most expert in the art of natation to venture out of their depth here is undoubtedly a rash proceeding. As a mater of fact, it is doubtful whether one of these would be permitted to do this, even if he had the inclination. The authorities are both cautious and watchful. Scattered along the beach are stalwart men, in dark-hued costumes that are practically bathing costumes, who bear coils of rope in their hands. Their mission is to safeguard the lives of the bathers. These *"bañeros"* are undoubtedly very fine fellows, and can count many a prolonged existence to their credit. At times, however, the enthusiasm for their profession would seem entirely to overpower them. On such occasions they will dash in amongst the waves and rescue a bather by force, quite regardless of whether he considers himself in need of assistance or not. It is useless for the latter to protest. When the *bañeros* are moved to action they will be satisfied with nothing less than dragging him ashore in triumph. And then follows a certain mortal obligation concerning a reward which even the most strong-minded finds difficult to resist under the circumstances.

The arrangements for bathing accommodation are good throughout Mar del Plata. There is no necessity here too be cooped up on one of those small, dark, movable prisons that still obtain in England. The bathing houses are picturesque, roomy, and have as a rule the very pleasant advantage of a verandah in front. The price of this accommodation, moreover, which averages fifty centavos (ten pence), is decidedly cheap when compared with the rates which prevail in Mar del Plata in general.

There is a tradition that this present vogue of sea-bathing was instituted many years ago by an English seaman who, shipwrecked, landed at the spot. The occurrence happened at that period when the Argentines themselves had just discovered the pleasurable possibilities of the spot. The sailor, alive to his opportunity, decided to make the place his home. In due course he became the proprietor of the very first bathing establishment. From the excessive popularity that he won for himself it seems likely that he must have graduated at a watering place at home. One can imagine him well – the "salt" turned longshoreman, cajoling the then inexpert Argentines into their natatory efforts in the bluff yet winning manner of his kind! He is reported to have made a fortune over the business, and it is likely enough that he did. One thing is certain however. If he, or his shade, we re ever to return to Mar del Plata at the present moment, its glorified aspects would astonish him not a little.

The sands of Mar del Plata at the height of its season afford as gay a scene as that which any continental watering place can display. Nurses and children beneath the shade of tents, entertainers, salesmen, and bathers – all these are here in their hundreds. Here and there are the coastguards, dark of face for the most part, who, with their cutlasses at their side, make a brave parade amidst the gaily dressed throng.

The Argentine seaside resort is emphatically no place for the owner of a slim purse. The evidence of this is forthcoming at the very moment of arrival. Porters here are wont to look askance at a "tip" which in Buenos Aires would be accepted with gratitude. In the station yard, too, it is unwise to attempt to bargain with a cabman, at any rate during the season. The consequences of such misplaced caution are wont to be lamentable. The Jehu will refuse with contempt to enter into any negotiations whatever. He will take a passenger on his own terms, and will make a favour of the proceeding even then. If the matter be not immediately clinched, he, together with the rest of his fellow benefactors, will be overwhelmed with the general exodus from the station. A little later the whole army of cabs will have departed, bearing off a host of less cautiously minded persons, and leaving a number of stranded and chastened folk to await the leisurely return of the vehicles with such patience as is vouchsafed them.

The cost of hotel life in Mar del Plata is on a par with all else. The obtaining of a room, moreover, is not always such an easy matter, although the place is well provided with good hotels. By far the largest of these is the *Hotel Bristol*, a caravansarai that is probably the best in South America. The establishment consists of a main building, with a couple of annexes, one on either hand. In these latter, which each occupy a square in the town, are situated the bedrooms. The main building is by far the most imposing of the three. Here is the dining-room, a magnificent apartment, while next to it is a large entertainment hall, upholstered and decorated in a gorgeous style, which, containing a stage at one end, is used for the purposes of dances, concerts and theatricals at will.

Upon the other side of a broad terrace is the Casino. Part and parcel of the hotel's establishment, it has modelled its ethics upon those of the European gaming centres. In order to gain admittance to the inner rooms, however, where roulette is played, a fee of ten dollars, which serves as a pass for one night or for the length of the season alike, is charged. Entrance to the outer room, devoted to the interests of *petits-chevaux*, is free to all. But the amounts risked here are paltry, compared to the sums which change hands in the inner sanctum. There is a system in vogue in this haunt of high play that is lacking in most of the European places of this kind. It is possible to obtain as an equivalent for money a number of counters of a particular colour – those that have the highest face value are very pretty playthings of mother of pearl. By this means confusion as to the ownership of a steak is to a great extent obviated, and the methods of sharpers in this respect rendered useless. The croupiers here are as decorous and sphinxlike as any at Monte Carlo. In view of the salary they receive (over forty pounds per month) there is no reason why they should not be.

The scene upon the terrace at night is extremely pretty. The place is thronged with the visitors, more especially just after the dinner hour. It is the favourite promenade of the ladies. And these, gliding to and fro with Argentine grace in the brilliant glow of the electric light, afford serious rivalry to the attractions of the tables within. But, sad to relate, it is seldom that the latter do not prove the more powerful magnates in the end.

There is one rather curious custom prevailing at the Bristol Hotel, which is worthy of mention. At the entrance to the large dining-hall one is confronted by a number of fruit sellers who offer baskets filled with every variety of the produce. The visitor, having purchased one of these, carries it with him to his table and partakes of its contents for the desert. The custom appeals as a pleasant one at first; the baskets are inviting and the choice large. But after a while it occurs to the visitor to demand why the hotel itself does not follow the usual Argentine system of providing fruit with *table d'hôte* meals. An Englishman connected with the Company informed me that the reason lay in the fact that the Argentines had formerly been accustomed to help themselves with such freedom to the fruit that none but the very poor specimens were left over for the remaining guests. A little later an Argentine favoured me with a similar version – in fact the same, with the exception that the blame for over-indulgence was laid in this case at the foreigner's door. Neither explanation seemed convincing. Indeed, it appeared a little obvious that the difficulty might have been overcome by a more generous supply of good fruit. Few, however, who come to the Bristol are given to object to such extras as these, for the hotel is palatial and the cuisine excellent.

The Hotel Bristol in Mar del Plata no longer exists. In 1938 it was replaced by the Casino Central, built between Plaza Bristol and Playa Bristol. According to James, this is a huge emporium, one of the largest gaming houses in the world containing hundreds of slot machines and tables. In fact, he told me when we met up after his visit, that was where he spent his last night in the resort.

"But you never gamble," I pointed out. Not only had he always frowned on my own occasional flutters, he didn't even approve of buying shares.

It was December and we were bundled up in thick jackets and scarves heading across the park to get a pint before lunch. A thermal hat was pulled half over James's ears. The Argentine Riviera seemed a long way away.

"You should have seen me." He gave an exalted skip. "Not only was I playing the slots, but I was putting money on the roulette tables, on hunches, on single numbers. James Bond style."

"Single numbers are thirty-seven-to-one." I couldn't think of a more unlikely James Bond.

He shook his head and laughed. "I don't know about the maths. But I do know I picked a couple of winners, and ended up with ten thousand dollars."

"What!"

"Which was just as well, because I had dipped into one of my charities for funds." He gave a hooting laugh. "I was twenty thousand dollars down at one point."

Shocked, I stared at him, but he didn't slow his pace. He was showing off to me as he used to at school when he had done well in class, or on the sports field. Since then, I had become used to thinking of him as a safe, law-abiding, charity-working, North London family man. Now he had revealed a side of himself I had not been aware of.

"What did you think you were doing? If you'd blown the charity finds, you'd have been sacked and more than likely gone to jail. Do you have no sense of... anything?"

"It was such a wonderful gamble." He clearly liked the word "gamble" and another little skip broke his confident stride. "That was the real thrill, the *real* thrill. There was a strange, almost euphoric atmosphere in Mar del Plata. It's hard to explain. It was such a weird time, with the American president arriving like a Martian from outer space, and the great sod-off security fences keeping the proletariat out. It was pure science fiction. How many millions did all this cost, and what did these world leaders know about how anybody lived? Suddenly money seemed like a joke. It made me want to throw it all away – dollars, euros, pesos – just to show how senseless the whole thing was."

"Money is the root of all economics," I pointed out, "the whole basis of our social existence. I don't suppose the recipients of your charity think it's senseless. How could you ever expose their funds to such a risk?"

"Perhaps it's just part of the mystery of being human."

"You're certainly a mystery to me."

He put his arm round my shoulder in that patronising way he sometimes has, and turned on his Maradona accent. "*Hombre*, don't worry. All life is a mystery, and a gamble, too, a constant battle between pleasure and pain. Here..." Reaching inside his jacket he produced a couple of cigars. "Why don't you relax, and try one of these babies."

I took the huge Havana and wetted its end on my grinning lips. There was hope for him after all.

11: THE EPONYMOUS CITY

Bristol Tourist Office
Bristol, England
www.visitbristol.co.uk

The first time I visited Bristol was in late 2001, when the West Country port city was proposing to put in a bid to become the European Capital of Culture in 2008. I had been called in as a consultant to help formulate the bid and had just thirty hours in the city. Sophie had not long packed her bags and I was doing my best to avoid our empty London flat, flying directly in from Oporto on the Wednesday afternoon and out to Brussels on the Thursday evening. Bristol had been short listed for the European title, but in the end it was to lose out to Liverpool, the other British slaving port.

There is, I discovered, no Hotel Bristol in Bristol. There is a Thistle Bristol, Bristol Marriott, Hilton Bristol, Ramada Plaza Bristol and Jurys Bristol, but no Bristol *per se*. Perhaps it would be too much. After all, London has no great London Hotel, Paris no Paris nor New York a New York. Lord Bristol, Bishop of Derry, once or twice took the waters at Bristol Wells, but he otherwise had nothing to do with the place from which his family took its name. John Hervey, the first Earl of Bristol, had simply chosen his title from a basket of eleven defunct titles going begging when he was elevated to the peerage by King George I for his support in bringing the Hanoverians to the throne. This was not our Earl Bristol's father John Hervey, but a more distant relation who came from East Anglia and bought the Suffolk estate at Ickworth as well as the family's London home in St James's Square.

If Bristol the city, and not Bristol the lord, is responsible for providing the world with a glamorous name for hotels, it is not immediately obvious why. Pleasant though this West Country regional capital (pop 380,000) is, it is less vibrant than many historic ports: Amsterdam, say, or Seville, or Naples. Of course, it may well have been more impressive at the time when many Bristol hotels were being built, before the bombing raids of the Second World War blew it half to bits.

Bristol lies nine miles from the sea on the River Avon, which made it a safe haven for several hundred years and brought it prosperity as a transatlantic trading port. This prosperity depended on the river, which meandered unhelpfully and had such a discrepancy in tides that twice a day vessels were left to settle on the mud – "ship shape and Bristol fashion". To overcome the problem, the New Cut was dug to the south to take the tidal river, and locks were built to control the flow of water on its original course through the city, allowing a permanent high tide in a "floating harbour". It didn't help. As ships grew larger they were in danger of getting stuck in the mud or even breaking their backs in the meandering journey to the Bristol Channel and the sea.

There were a number of trade routes that scattered the city's name around the world. In the middle ages, for instance, Bristol was famous for wine, which daily poured on to its quaysides in such quantities that it became known as "Bristol milk". It arrived on ships trading with the Continental Atlantic seaboard from Aquitaine to Cádiz and today the city is twinned with both Bordeaux and Oporto. In order to survive the long sea voyage, some wines were given extended lives by blending with brandy, which was how port from Porto in Portugal and sherry, the fortified wine from Jerez in Spain, came to be popular way beyond their vineyards of origin. As a major importer, Bristol's name became irrevocably linked to sherry. It certainly had a place in the store cupboard of America's first lady: Martha Washington's sherry crab soup called specifically for Bristol sherry, as did her cakes.

Towards the end of the nineteenth century, a new blend of sweet oloroso sherry was formulated by John Harvey, son of the John Harvey who gave a local wine importing business its name and nothing to do with the Herveys of Ickworth. Harvey's of Bristol, the wine importers, were founded in 1796 and had premises in Denmark Street where John Harvey II invited a woman dignitary visiting the medieval cellars to taste the established sherry and then to sample his experimental batch. "If the first one is Bristol milk," she is supposed to have exclaimed. "then this one is Bristol cream." It was an instant hit. By the late 20th century one in five bottles of sherry drunk worldwide was Harvey's Bristol Cream.

At the same time that America's most sociable first lady was serving her sherry-laced soup and Lord Bristol was roaming the Continent demanding nothing less than first-class accommodation, there were more than 500 drinking houses in Bristol, many of them run by former sailors and some with rooms or straw mattresses for rent. One of these was the half-timbered Llandoger Trow, still in existence and now unromantically attached to a Travel Inn. It was here that the marooned sailor Alexander Selkirk told his tale to Daniel Defoe, inspiring him to write *Robinson Crusoe*.

In Lord Bristol's day, a traveller in Britain might stay at one of the coaching inns that had become well established not just for necessary commercial traffic but for tourists, too, especially since the politics of Europe made Continental travel difficult. London society and the wealthy of indifferent health decamped for the summer, and headed for the spa at Bath a dozen miles up the road, or to the fashionable Clifton Downs just above Bristol where they would take the Bristol waters. At their points of arrival travellers might find themselves besieged with offers of accommodation by locals with rooms to rent, much as people do at marine terminals or bus and train stations in many parts of the world today.

Aristocrats such as the Bristols, on the other hand, had long been able to guarantee a good night when they journeyed around Britain, because they were able to call on any country house, where they might expect to be put up even in the absence of the owner. They would stay the night, expect to be fed, and tip the staff in the morning, which is the origin of tipping in hotels. In Bristol's inns there was good food to accompany the abundant wine. Ships docked with new delicacies, such as turtles, which made a popular soup. It was on the menu every day at the Bush in Corn Street, the city's largest 19th-century coaching inn. In fact travellers complained that they were in constant danger of tripping over these helpless creatures as they waited their fate in the pot. The Bush's Christmas menu was famous. Nearly a yard long, it contained more than a hundred and fifty dishes.

But however appetising the food, the Bush, like most c o a c h i n g inns, could not compete with the railways and it did not see out the century. The railways came a couple of decades after the Battle of Waterloo brought peace to Eu rope and the resumption of Continental travel. The well-off rediscove red the Grand Tour, palatial hotels we re built and spas we re found to be a particularly efficacious way of flushing the wallets of the rich. The accompanying staff of the travelling rich would be offered pension arrangements either in a hotel garret or in a separate lodging nearby. It has been suggested that the Tremont on Boston in egalitarian, prog ressive America, was the first to put a full-time domestic staff at the service of every guest. That was in 1829, twenty-six years after Lord Bristol's death. (He died, incidentally, in a miserable barn north of Rome; seized with stomach pains, he had been given shelter in a wayside cottage but when his hosts realised he was a Protestant bishop, and not a particularly pious one at that, they bundled him into an outhouse where he expired, his final words unre co rded and a matter between him and his hopefully patient and forgiving god.)

Britain's first inter-city railway linked London with Bristol in an attempt to halt loss of trade to Liverpool, which was overtaking it as Britain's second port. It was not a universally popular scheme. The Duke of Wellington, erstwhile prime minister and high Tory, was completely opposed to it, declaring, "It will only encourage the lower classes to move about." But Isambard Kingdom Brunel won the day, built the railway and became irrevocably associated with the city. The engineer's idea was to have grand hotels, fully staffed, at each end of his Great Western Railway, in Paddington and Temple Meads, and this was to be the route by which Londoners would travel to New York. The vessel he designed to take them across the Atlantic was the SS Great Britain. It was the largest propelled iron ship ever to set sail, a pioneer of international passenger travel and mass emigration.

Now extensively and imaginatively restored, the SS Great Britain has returned to the Bristol dry dock in the Floating Harbour where she was created. Nearby is a replica of John Cabot's caravel, Matthew, launched for the 500th anniversary of the epic North Atlantic voyage in 1492, which was funded by the Bristol Society of Merchant Venturers. This made him the first European officially to set foot on the American continent and the first to raise the flag in what was to become the British Empire – never mind that, like Columbus, he was probably Genoese.

The SS Great Britain and the Matthew took the name of their city of origin to the New World and the thirty-four Bristol towns in North America are spread from Québec to California. Outside North America, however, no other town in the British Empire took the name of Bristol. This may be because the port became associated with the slave trade, although the Portuguese slave trading port of Lagos gave its name to Nigeria's capital. (The Lagos Bristol in Nigeria briefly hit the headlines in 1947 when a black British civil servant was refused a room, and again in 1976, when a woman accused of being a witch was stoned to death by a mob in the hotel grounds.)

The British Empire and Commonwealth Museum is housed in Brunel's railway terminal at Temple Meads. It is full of tales of Bristol men who travelled to the ends of the earth – explorers, wine merchants, slave traders, merchant venturers, Company men, missionaries, district officers – all endeavouring to make their mark on the world.

Nobody at the museum knows why the name of Bristol should have become popular among hotel owners, however. Nor do the city library archivists, nor the councillors who work in the offices built by Brunel to be the railway hotel. The only direct connection between Bristol and hotels that I could discover was that in 2000 a group of local businessmen opened a smart new hotel at Sheffield in Yorkshire, and because of their roots they called it the Bristol.

But otherwise that is all that I know about Bristol and why the name of the city might have been so widely distributed about the world. It is more than any man should want to know. And any woman, too, though I was unable to tell Sophie exactly why Bristol City, the town or the football club, should be the chosen source of Cockney rhyming slang for "titty" – such a grubby word for a thing so divine.

Yet I can't help thinking that her Bristols are just one part of her that I sorely miss.

12: POSTCARDS FROM MARK TWAIN

Hotel Bristol
York Street, Colombo, Ceylon
(No longer standing)

It can be no exaggeration to say that my collection of postcards, luggage labels, matches, menus, brochures, ashtrays, keyrings, soaps, shower caps and other memorabilia of Bristol hotels was the largest in the world. But it was the postcards that I liked best. Dating from the 1880s to the present day, they included views of interiors long since refurbished, views that have been lost to new buildings and traffic, and many fine buildings no longer standing. It was a wonderful visual story of a small but not insignificant aspect of the hospitality industry.

For several years I spent my spare time rummaging through boxes on market stalls, visiting bric-à-brac and antiquarian bookshops, trawling the internet and making regularly visits to eBay, developing a network of worldwide suppliers. At first, whenever I stayed in a Bristol, I would send a postcard of the hotel to Sophie, but when I realised that she was throwing them away, I addressed them to myself at the London office.

Sophie never understood the excitement of collecting nor did she appreciate the increasing value of these acquisitions. I promised her that I would get rid of them as soon as I could find a suitable archive or depository, but the real reason I procrastinated is that I had other plans for the Tom Cotton Collection. Once I could be sure that I had a postcard of eve ry Hotel Bristol that ever existed, I intended to locate them all on a map of the world and have them mounted for a travelling exhibition that could go on display in the foyers of eve ry hotel called Bristol around the world.

Of course I don't know what happened to the postcards in the end, and probably never will find out, but nothing would make me happier than one day walking into a Hotel Bristol and seeing my idea brought to fruition.

Among my collection were several old postcards of the Hotel Bristol in Colombo, Sri Lanka, or what was then Ceylon, and the frequency with which these turned up is not surprising because A.W.A. Plâté, the man who took the pictures, had his photographic studio in the hotel. A handsome colonial building in the Raffles mould, the Bristol Hotel on the postcard was in a dusty looking street with no traffic except for an unoccupied rickshaw that stood in the shade of a jacaranda. Nothing much was going on. It appeared to be a very restful spot and I am sure that it would have been a pleasure to sip a pink gin beneath its pavement awning, or settle down to a curry from the *"Best cuisine in the East – Curries a Speciality"*. This boast, in English, French and German, is on a hand-coloured card in my possession, which adds the further claim that room rates were moderate". Even from this distance I can hear the gentle cajoling of a white-jacketed waiter touting for custom, and I am beguiled by his sales pitch.

The Hotel Bristol no longer exists, but the name of the man who took the pictures is immortalised in millions of postcards of the hotel, the island and other parts of Asia. A.W.A. Plâté was an apothecary before he was a photographer. He his wife Clara set up a studio in the hotel in 1890 and the pictures and postcards they produced for guests and local tourists over the following two years as they travelled around Southeast Asia were so successful that the couple moved to a building in Colpetty, which they named the Bristol Studio. This became the finest photographic establishment in the East, and it was soon producing half a million postcards a year. Plâté & Co was in business at the same address until 1974.

There is something evocative about black-and-white photography. It is a mature medium that conveys both innocence and honesty, showing not just another time but a place and people without time. Images are completely trapped in the frame with no wish or way to escape. How many hotels and travellers' haunts were photographed like this, in crisp monochrome, their streets ignorant of traffic jams, the unhurried people made for the early cameras' long exposures? In even the smallest villages around the world today bars and cafés like to put up enlarged prints of postcards showing how their communities looked, how their people dressed, before they were discoloured by industry, wars, tourism and homogenous clothing. Though Hungary's was the first postal system to accept the idea of postcards, it was the picture of Gustav Eiffel's astonishing Tower in the Paris Exhibition of 1889, celebrating the centenary of the French Revolution, that began seriously to fill mail bags, inscribed with spidery writing so familiar to relatives and so hard for us to decipher today. *I have been here, and seen this. This is my hotel.*

This is not to say that colour photography is not wonderful. But by the time it appeared the world was becoming a different place. The contrast between the two provided an dividing line, throwing the monochrome world into the past and giving it a patina of romance. Perhaps we like to think of the past without colour, just as we like our Greek and Roman temples unpainted, not gaudy as they really were. Black-and-white studio portraits are the images we have our great grandparents, and it is often the way we picture famous people, too, even colourful artists like Monet and Matisse.

I imagine Mark Twain in black-and-white. His grizzled thick grey hair and walrus whiskers were made for monochrome. The creator of Tom Sawyer and Huckleberry Finn stayed at the Hotel Bristol in Colombo at the same time that A.W.A. Plâté started taking photographs. He was on a world lecture tour of the British Empire, as a lack of linguistic skills prevented him from entertaining non-English speaking audiences. He needed the money because he had just lost $100,000 investing in a worthless venture concerning a typesetting machine. It is not difficult to imagine him in a white linen suit, dusting off his hat and settling down at the bar with a bourbon, his unruly hair tickled by the cooling draughts of the ceiling fan. All in monochrome.

He wrote down his experience of the journey in *Follow the*

Equator, published in 1896, and it is clear that he saw the Bristol Hotel, the town, its people and the whole island of Serendipity not as a monotonous postcard, but in a blindingly colourful light:

January 13. Unspeakably hot. The equator is arriving again. We are within eight degrees of it. Ceylon present. Dear me, it is beautiful! And most sumptuously tropical, as to character of foliage and opulence of it. "What though the spicy breezes blow soft o'er Ceylon's isle" – an eloquent line, an incomparable line; it says little, but conveys whole libraries of sentiment, and Oriental charm and mystery, and tropic deliciousness – a line that quivers and tingles with a thousand unexpressed and inexpressible things, things that haunt one and find no articulate voice… Colombo, the capital. An Oriental town, most manifestly; and fascinating.

January 14. Hotel Bristol. Servant Brompy. Alert, gentle, smiling, winning young brown creature as ever was. Beautiful shining black hair combed back like a woman's, and knotted at the back of his head – tortoise-shell comb in it, sign that he is a Singhalese; slender, shapely form; jacket; under it is a beltless and flowing white cotton gown – from neck straight to heel; he and his outfit quite unmasculine. It was an embarrassment to undress before him.

We drove to the market, using the Japanese *jinriksha* – our first acquaintanceship with it. It is a light cart, with a native to draw it. He makes good speed for half-an-hour, but it is hard work for him; he is too slight for it. After the half-hour there is no more pleasure for you; your attention is all on the man, just as it would be on a tired horse, and necessarily your sympathy is there too. There's a plenty of these *'rickshas*, and the tariff is incredibly cheap…

The drive through the town and out to the Galle Face by the seashore, what a dream it was of tropical splendors of bloom and blossom, and Oriental conflagrations of costume! The walking groups of men, women, boys, girls, babies – each individual was a flame, each group a house afire for color. And such stunning colors, such intensely vivid colors, such rich and exquisite minglings and fusings of rainbows and lightnings! And all harmonious, all in perfect taste; never a discordant note; never a color on any person swearing at another color on him or failing to harmonize faultlessly with the colors of any group the wearer might join. The stuffs were silk-thin, soft, delicate, clinging; and, as a rule, each piece a solid color: a splendid green, a splendid blue, a splendid yellow, a splendid purple, a splendid ruby, deep, and rich with smouldering fires they swept continuously by in crowds and legions and multitudes, glowing, flashing, burning, radiant; and every five seconds came a burst of blinding red that made a body catch his breath, and filled his heart with joy. And then, the unimaginable grace of those costumes! Sometimes a woman's whole dress was but a scarf wound about her person and her head, sometimes a man's was but a turban and a careless rag or two - in both cases generous areas of polished dark skin showing – but always the arrangement compelled the homage of the eye and made the heart sing for gladness.

I can see it to this day, that radiant panorama, that wilderness of rich color, that incomparable dissolving-view of harmonious tints, and lithe half-covered forms, and beautiful brown faces, and gracious and graceful gestures and attitudes and movements, free, unstudied, barren of stiffness and restraint, and – Just then, into this dream of fairyland and paradise a grating dissonance was injected.

Out of a missionary school came marching, two and two, sixteen prim and pious little Christian black girls, Europenly clothed – dressed, to the last detail, as they would have been dressed on a summer Sunday in an English or American village. Those clothes – oh, they were unspeakably ugly! Ugly, barbarous, destitute of taste, destitute of grace, repulsive as a shroud. I looked at my womenfolk's clothes – just full-grown duplicates of the outrages disguising those poor little abused creatures – and was ashamed to be seen in the street with them. Then I looked at my own clothes, and was ashamed to be seen in the street with myself.

However, we must put up with our clothes as they are – they have their reason for existing. They are on us to expose us – to advertise what we wear them to conceal. They are a sign; a sign of insincerity; a sign of suppressed vanity; a pretense that we despise gorgeous colors and the graces of harmony and form; and we put them on to propagate that lie and back it up. But we do not deceive our neighbor; and when we step into Ceylon we realize that we have not even deceived ourselves. We do love brilliant colors and graceful costumes; and at home we will turn out in a storm to see them when the procession goes by – and envy the wearers. We go to the theater to look at them and grieve that we can't be clothed like that. We go to the King's ball, when we get a chance, and are glad of a sight of the splendid uniforms and the glittering orders. When we are granted permission to attend an imperial drawing-room we shut ourselves up in private and parade around in the theatrical court-dress by the hour, and admire ourselves in the glass, and are utterly happy; and every member of every governor's staff in democratic America does the same with his grand new uniform – and if he is not watched he will get himself photographed in it, too. When I see the Lord Mayor's footman I am dissatisfied with my lot. Yes, our clothes are a lie, and have been nothing short of that these hundred years. They are insincere, they are the ugly and appropriate outward exposure of an inward sham and a moral decay.

The last little brown boy I chanced to notice in the crowds and swarms of Colombo had nothing on but a twine string around his waist, but in my memory the frank honesty of his costume still stands out in pleasant contrast with the odious flummery in which the little Sunday-school dowdies were masquerading.

Of course you couldn't write all that on the back of a postcard. You would have to send an email. But electronic mail doesn't give you the full picture, and nobody is interested in collecting it.

13: BEHIND THE WHEEL
WITH LKJ SETRIGHT

Bristol Cars
Bristol, England
www.bristolcars.co.uk

My father loves well-made things: clothes, furniture, clocks, gadgets, buildings, fences, window catches, plugs, signage, anything that anyone has taken the trouble to think about and make. Things that other people don't notice will often receive his undivided attention, which isn't surprising after a career as a design consultant. Most of his work was commercial: offices, public buildings and government contracts that included a couple of overseas embassies. For some years he sat on the board of the Design Council and now and then he would be quoted in the Press. Mother is design conscious, too. A trained ceramicist, she had a craft shop in St Albans where James and I would help out in the holidays. This is where I discovered my appetite for book-keeping, and I did all her accounts. James inherited the family's artistic side, which passed me by, though I have always insisted that finance can be as creative as any art.

Dad's interest in well-made products ran to cars, and in later years he always drove a soft-top Saab. By the time James and I were ten, not only were we the best dressed children in our street, but we possessed a precocious knowledge of British motor manufacturing, being able to engage in any discussion about Jaguars, Alvises, Jenson Interceptors and, of course, Bristols.

Bristol cars are made at Filton, four miles north of Bristol, an engineering town centred on the aerodrome where the Bristol Aviation Company and its descendants have lived since 1910. It was here that the Boxkite, Blehheim, Beaufort, Beafighter, Brigand, Brabazon and Britannia took to the air, and it was here, on November 23, 2003, that Concorde was brought, after its final flight, to be put on show in a proposed aviation museum. Progressing from B to C, Bristol had supplied the supersonic anglo-French aircraft with its engine.

The achievements of the aviation company were appreciated in both war and peace, but immediately after the Second World War it faced a quandary. Military aircraft were no longer required, peacetime aircraft had yet to find their market and Filton had a battalion of skilled engineers turning up to work each day wanting something to do. In vanquished Europe, the future of some of the world's most important motor manufacturing companies was up for discussion. Famously, the British government declined to take over Volkswagen, believing the vehicles had no future, but the engineers at Filton were interested in the Bavarian motor manufacturers BMW, and they acquired the rights to its engines, which powered the first car to be produced by Bristol Aviation's new Car Division. The two-litre Bristol 400, which quickly resulted, was considered to be the most aerodynamically efficient car ever produced. It didn't even have door handles. Bristol continued, and continues, to make bespoke motors at Filton. Britain's last independent motor manufacturer has no dealerships, just one show room in London, and it turns out around a hundred vehicles a year, though the exact number is not a matter for public knowledge. These sell for between £250,000 and £400,000 a piece, and they have many admirers.

One of Bristol cars' greatest fans was L.K.J. (Lionel) Setright, the eccentric motoring journalist and editor of *Car* magazine, who died in 2005 after expressing his opinions in print for a third of a century. With the looks of Rasputin and the dress sense of Cecil Beaton, smoking only Sobranie Black Russians and driving far too fast for many of his passengers' tastes, Setright was a character indeed. There were many bees under his bonnet, and he was acknowledged for his ability to understand the finer points of engineering in an age when engineering was regarded as neither as interesting nor as sexy as design.

Setright wrote several books including *Drive On: A Social History of the Motor Car*, published in 2003, *Bristol Cars and Engines* (1974) and in *A Private Car – An Account of the Bristol*, a limited edition in two volumes: *The Word*, detailing every make of Bristol, and *The Image*, containing commissioned and historic photographs. Nine hundred copies were printed and sold at £300 each, and a hundred special editions with a numbered aluminium plaque cost £600.

I bought a special edition for my father for his seventieth birthday, and was sorry I could not have given him the real thing. The occasion was celebrated with a family gathering over a long weekend in my parents' villa on the Costa del Sol and inevitably over dinner talk turned to the family's early sorties to Spain. My parents made their first journeys into the Iberian peninsula in an assortment of exciting vehicles before James and I were born, at which point they traded in their two-seater Triumph Herald for one of the new Mark I Ford Escort and a green Dormobile. This house on wheels headed south from Hertfordshire each summer, the spacious interior full of games to keep James and myself amused. When the Pyreneees were sighted my father would sing *Lady of Spain I adore you* and my mother would respond with *I'm one of the nuts that come from Barcelona*. Once across the border, we would whoop and call for a halt at a beach. We didn't stay at hotels; either we couldn't afford to or it never occurred to us. We just camped for three or four nights en route before arriving at some half deserted piece of coast to spend a fortnight by the sea. I don't recall any motorways, and roads often led through small villages where there were chicken and donkeys to negotiate.

Looking at my father now, with his thinning voice and shining bald head, I realise that he must have seen quite a change in the world. Since his retirement he had become reflective and I sensed he had started living a little in the past, not least because he had begun to collect old travel books, which fill several shelves in his study. One is reserved for the books that James and I have found and sent him.

Spain, Dad has often pointed out, was one of the last countries in Europe to embrace tourism. Even Thomas Cook, who pioneered mass tourism in Europe, to France, Switzerland, Germany, Italy, Greece, Egypt and the Holy Land, did not venture over the Pyrenees until late in the day. Most of the peninsula remained pre-industrial, if not medieval, until the late 20th century when it was rocketed into the modern world as Europe's Florida.

Spain's limitations were certainly evident in Lord Bristol's times. When he was on his travels, he was following well known Grand Tour paths to the Classical sights of central southern Europe. Few were tempted to explore the legacy of Greece and Rome on the far side of the Pyrenees where the roads were dire. In 1789, however, the Earl-Bishop found himself in revolutionary France, and he headed for the south to avoid the violent anti-clericalism that was about to bring down the power of the Church. As a bishop, he opposed the revolutionaries but as a man of liberal opinions he was not at first entirely against them, believing that the division of France between a Republican North and a Royalist South might be the best way forward. With his back to the Pyrenean wall, he began to plan a winter in Spain, "*'tis a favourite country with me, for its climate, its manners, & its Natural History w'ch as yet is Vierge – parfaitement Pucelle*" – virgin, perfectly pure. Travelling with the Catholic Irish Abbé O'Cassidi, he was free of gout and in high spirits. "*We have five saddle horses for the journey is long; I have two led for myself – as soon as we pass Perpignan we shall find a perpetual sunshine, & such a succession of new objects as cannot fail to benefit the mind as much as the body. Our project is to coast it by land (bien entendue) by Gibraltar, Andalusia, peep into Don Quixote's country, return by the Algarve, Lisbon, Oporto, Gil Blas, Salamanca and Ovideo, thro' Biscay to Bayonne & Bordeaux.*"

In the end, he was forced to conclude that, tireless horseman and adventurer that he was, the roads were just too bad and, worse, the accommodation would not come up to the Bristol

standard. It was only after his death that Britons began to pour
into the peninsula in the red coats of Wellington's army to end five
years of occupation by the French. It was another two decades
before Washington Irving's bestseller, *Tales of the Alhambra*, alerted
the world to the romance of Spain. The year it was published an
Englishman called Richard Ford was travelling the peninsula on
his horse, Jaca Cordovese, making notes that John Murray would
persuade him to turn into the first tourist guide to the country,
The Hand Book For Spain, which came out in 1848. There were
no hotel listings. The Bristol hotels, in Madrid, Barcelona, Seville,
Benidorm, even Gibraltar, would come much later. In Ford's day
there were simply *ventas, mesones, posadas* or *paradores*, large
country inns where horses could be stabled, situated every thirty
miles or so on roads little altered since the Roman occupation.
They were based on the Roman *stabulum*, and the *caravansari* or
han of Persia and the east, and were principally intended for the
accommodation of cattle and horses on the ground floor, with
rooms for travellers above. Like the feudal lords of medieval
castles, landlords were obliged to provide the guests with nothing
more than salt and fire. Only in towns could a 19th-century
traveller find a *fonda* (from the Arabic *funduqs*), where he might
sleep and be served something to eat.

This, according to Setright, was still the Dark Ages in Europe,
a period that lasted from the fall of Rome in the 6th century until
the arrival of the motorcar, which in the case of Spain was really
not until the 20th century. In 1903, half a dozen years after the
first city-to-city road races were started in France and Germany, a
race was organised from Paris to Madrid to blaze a trail into the
fusty donkey lands of Iberia and introduce the glamorous new
motor sport. But the race reached no further than Bordeaux.
Unmarshalled, spectators had no idea that standing in front of
motor cars was not the best way to view them, and drivers were
so blinded by the dust stirred up by their 100km-per-hour-plus
vehicles that they navigated by looking skyward and following the
tops of the avenues of trees. The first cars in Bordeaux – some of

their occupants had booked into the city's Hotel Bristol in Place Gambetta – waited to hear what had happened to the rest of the field. News of carnage soon began to arrive. The tally of dead and injured was never recorded, though among the known dead drivers and mechanics was Marcel Renault, one of the two brothers who had started the French motor manufacturers. When news reached Madrid, the reception committee stood down. The world had failed to drive a path to its door. Perhaps it was as well. Had the race continued into the pot-holed roads of Spain, who knows what further disasters might have occurred.

Some intrepid drivers did begin to get through. My father's travel book collection includes a copy of *Spain in a Two-Seater* by an Englishman, Halford Ross. He and his wife were thirty miles from Zaragosa, travelling homeward on the high *meseta* in the summer of 1925: "*We were silent in that realm of silence, for to speak would have broken a spell that seemed to overawe everything. My wife was driving very slowly – not more than seven or eight miles an hour, fortunately; for the going was atrocious – waves of hard stones alternating with transverse ridges. Ahead was a small oasis of trees, some of which extended and bordered the track and looked most refreshing. These we had reached when I heard a bouncing and thumping going on underneath the car. Looking out over the left-hand side I saw a bar of steel swinging and banging from side to side beneath us and I called out to stop. To our horror we found that the offside connecting rod steering arm had snapped and the front wheel couple was loose, the steering smashed, the car out of action.*"

Breaking down was always a possibility. Even when we were on our family holidays in the early 1970s, we would expect a few hours, even a day or two, lost to mechanical failure. Parts would be forged back into shape by a smithy, for in Spain, as in most of the world, it was often the local blacksmith who took on the pioneer role of the garage, as they did for Harold Ross. The broken ends of his connecting rod were heated at a forge, pressed together and quenched in cold water, making the steel stronger than ever.

Muirhead's Blue Guide of 1935 is another volume from my

father's shelves. It has a language section with an A–Z for motorists, from "Back-fire" (*explosión en el carburador*) to "Wrench, monkey" (*llaveinglesa – English key*). Another book from the thirties was Charles L Freeston's *The Roads of Spain: a 5,000-mile journey in the new touring paradise*, with an introduction by H.E. The Marquess de Merry del Val, GVCO. Its aim was clearly to reassure motorists that there was no reason to fear broken springs from the roads, a prospect that had for so long deterred British and American visitors from venturing on to the peninsula. Photographs showed the author's convertible Rolls-Royce in empty streets in both town and country. The car is pictured on the open road, static, with no driver, and the caption: "*A characteristic corner, banked, widened and with parapet*". The picture beneath records: "*The same corner from below*".

A Ministry of Tourism had been set up in Madrid in 1928 to encourage visitors, with the specific remit to provide accommodation for road travellers in historically interesting buildings, which were to become the state-run *paradores*. The ministry also established a series of Albergues de Carratera that were a day's car journey apart, which was then reckoned to be no more than 200 kilometres. Calculating that an Albergue might see up to three cars in a day, these early motels had eight rooms and nobody was allowed to stay for more than forty-eight hours, to keep the traffic moving. (In *Drive On*, Setright points out that about this time the word "Motel" was first used in the USA by a tourist cabin on Route 101 in California.)

Spain's Civil War and the subsequent war in Europe stalled any developments of the tourist infrastructure, but after Nato had welcomed Franco's fascist regime back into its fold in 1952, intrepid travellers began once more breasting the Pyrenees. Motorists were encouraged in unusual ways. The first Fodor travel guide to Spain, from 1957, has a photograph of a policeman at traffic lights in Madrid handing out glasses of sherry to drivers while they wait for the lights to change.

Early motorists often treated their vehicles with the same

degree of care that earlier travellers had extended to their horses, using garages like stables, places where their cars could be sheltered and refreshed overnight. Wilson MacArthur, author of *Auto Nomad in Spain*, used to seek out garages for his Wolsey, which he had christenend Huberta, with as much care as he selected his hotels. There is no photograph of him in the book, though I imagine he looked like my father. Perhaps that's because his wife, Joan, a pretty young woman with a full face and dark hair who appears in photographs with Huberta, reminds me a little of my mother.

Richard Ford, author of the 1848 *Handbook Book for Spain*, had complained bitterly about the introduction of passports by the French during their occupation of Spain. "*I hope the day will never come*," he wrote, "*when England is hindered with such trivia that are so against our natural birthright of liberty and locomotion.*" By the 20th century these hindrances had to be endured – or enjoyed. In *Auto Nomad in Spain*, the border customs control between France and Spain provided the MacArthurs with a dramatic introduction to an entirely new experience:

I drew up at the barrier that closed the road. The red, yellow and red flag of Spain – not of the Republic but of the Monarchy, although no monarch ruled in Spain – drooped in languid folds, a splash of brilliant colour against the greys and greens of the gorge, the biscuit-coloured buildings and the grey road. The air was still. It hummed with heat, the fierce baking heat of an April forenoon with no breeze. At the barrier which slices the village of Le Perthus in two the tempo of life changed abruptly.

While I went off to attend to formalities, Joan received her initiation into the Spanish scene. As she sat in the car two men in uniform emerged from the Spanish frontier post: frontier guards of some sort – for of course I was not familiar yet with the ramifications of officialdom in post-war Spain – and very smart in their khaki uniforms. They wore Ronald Coleman moustaches and had added to the dashing effect with short sideburns: but what first opened Joan's eyes was their startling foreignness. By no aberration of the imagination could these men be taken for Frenchmen. There was nothing French about them; and the contrast with the Frenchman of Perpignan and Le Perthus was arresting.

A wooden bar across the road can achieve an amazing transformation. They looked, with interest, at Huberta the car, large, black, shiny and dignified. They glanced at the neat pile of luggage on the roof; and they glanced inside and saw Joan. The effect was magical. They smiled, they saluted, they made friendly gestures; and then they leant their backs against the wall and the taller, more good-looking of the pair threw back his head and opened his mouth and broke into song. It was, I remember, *Ay, ay, ay*, a modern song; and he trolled it out in a clear, pleasing tenor with complete assurance and with an eye that periodically came down, under long lashes, to note the effect – an eye quizzical, humorous and very knowing.

At the end of it he gave a little bow in Joan's direction, then put his back against the wall again and sang again; and Joan sat enthralled, for it was quite impossible to imagine a British bobby serenading a foreign lady in a car at eleven o'clock in the morning at Dover or Southampton.

My parents did not cross this border until a decade or so later, but I like to imagine that this was how, in the first flush of their relationship, they were welcomed to Spain.

14: A MOTORING LESSON IN MACEDONIA

Hotel Bristol
Skopje, Former Yugoslav Republic of Macedonia
Tel: +389 91-114 883

"If you want a bed for the night, just head for the railway station. That's where you always find the hotels."

I remembered this advice on my first trip to Macedonia a couple of years ago. I had heard it many years earlier from Paul Shepherd, a friend of my father's, who in the Sixties regularly holidayed in Greece while my father was discovering Spain. He had studied engineering at Imperial College in London, as I recall, and he first took these Mediterranean holidays with some student friends. They would drive non-stop, taking thirty-six hours to reach Athens. There were usually three of four of them in an old Vauxhall or a Ford, and they would bat along without cease, not wanting to waste time on hotels en route. There was no coast road in Yugoslavia then, and only one main road through the whole country, most of it cobbled, single lane and unlit. It went straight through any town in its path.

"I remember the dawns," he said. "We took a few uppers, of course, to keep us awake, but I don't think I was hallucinating when those shadows came drifting out of the night, figures walking across the fields to work. I always think of them when people start talking about going back to an agrarian economy. Those ghostly shadows were a paean to weariness."

Paul's university education had been sponsored by BOAC, and after completing his course he was obliged to train to be a pilot, contracted to fly for the long-haul carrier for a certain number of years. This meant he had huge borrowing power against his potentially large salary and as soon as he could he bought himself an Austin Healey sports car, a classic soft-top in British racing green with leather upholstery, wooden dashboard and steering wheel and wire wall wheels, which was his pride and joy. It wasn't long afterwards that he was heading for Greece in the company of a girlfriend.

With a woman in tow, he was happy to spend nights in hotels, none of which he had booked in advance. Following his own dictum, each evening when he arrived at a town he would simply head for the railway station and take the pick of the bunch. "We didn't have guide books then," he told me and James. "Just a map of Europe and a tongue in our heads. There weren't any tourist offices either."

When they reached the town of Skopje in southern Yugoslavia, they once more made for the railway station, a showpiece designed by a Serbian architect called Gavrilovic and completed in 1940. Its Art Deco façade featured a large clock.

On Marshal Tito Street, the main avenue leading to the station, there were three hotels in a row and, according to Paul, it was his girlfriend who decided which one they should stay in by employing a childish game of elimination: "*One potato, two potato, three potato, four; five potato, six potato, seven potato more.*" Having pointed first to the hotel on the left, nearest the station, she ended with the one in the middle. So that's where they stayed. It was a warm evening in July, and though the hotel did not have parking facilities, the manager had said that the car, a little dusty from the trip, would be perfectly safe on the kerb right outside. Crime barely existed under the communist regime and there was only a smattering of other vehicles parked in this main street that led from the station to the central square by the river.

It was a warm evening and after dinner in the hotel the couple took a stroll down to the river where they had a night cap in the square beside the imposing building that was the Army Club. They did not venture over the old bridge towards the minarets of the Turkish quarter. This was all they intended to see of the city, because straight after breakfast the next morning they would be on their way again. The Greek border was barely two hours away, and Paul looked forward to arriving in style in his new car. Back in the hotel, they were soon in bed, but not before he had pulled back the curtains to have a final look at the real love in his life and make sure she was safe. That night, he claimed, he dreamed that he was flying a Lancaster bomber over Dresden.

The next thing he knew he was wide awake and the whole room was shaking. Windows, doors and furniture danced and rattled, pictures fell off walls, while glass crashed outside and masonry thundered to the ground. Leaping up, he rushed to the window in time to see the whole railway station fold in on itself, covering a train that was pulling into a platform. The Austin Healey was half covered in debris. The dawn light was turning grey with dust. Two young women in the street were running for their lives. Behind him, the whole room, the whole building seemed on the point of implosion.

A chilling silence followed. Then the rumbling came again. The earth's crust was tearing itself apart.

It was crystal clear to Paul that they should get out of the building as soon as they could. He managed to pull on his trousers, while his girlfriend wrapped herself in a sheet and they made their way along the corridor and down the stairs. Doors were being flung open and others were making their escape. People were shouting in Serbo-Croat, in German and Greek. The air was thick with plaster dust and the floors felt unsafe beneath their feet. The thunderous crash of brick and stone and the smashing of glass continued around them, but the hotel managed, heroically, to stay up and keep them safe. Out in the street, the scene was far worse than when he had glimpsed it from the window. There was no sign of his car and it was hard to see anything for the dust that now hung thick in the air. Though they had no way of knowing which way to go, Paul realised that they had to get away from every building that remained, because every one of them was about to collapse.

Scrambling over the pile of debris outside the hotel to reach the middle of the street, Paul caught his foot in wooden hoop that protruded from the rubble. He gave it a yank and found himself staring at the twisted steering wheel of his Austin Healey, which had otherwise completely disappeared. A small group of survivors was huddled in awe the middle of Marshal Tito Street and they could see from the stopped clock on what remained of the station's facade that the earthquake had struck at 5.17. The two hotels either side of theirs were no longer standing. The one nearest the station, the Macedonia, had caved in, split to the foundations and levelled in just five seconds, leaving hundreds of guests entombed.

The two young women Paul had seen from the window heading towards the station were in shock. They were from Germany, and had been on their way to the airport to catch a plane to Belgrade. They had left their hotel two minutes before it collapsed. The Yugoslav Airlines flight they were booked on was to be piloted by another lucky guest at their hotel, who had also left a few minutes before it collapsed. Others were not so fortunate. An English tourist who had managed to escape began desperately looking among the rubble, shouting out the name of his wife. Paul and the pilot joined the search.

It was hard to comprehend just how murderous the first shockwave had been. In just twenty seconds more than a thousand people died, more than 3,000 were seriously injured and nearly eighty percent of the city's population was made homeless. The silence that had followed the initial eruptions now began to be penetrated by screams and keening, as figures dressed in nightwear, or whatever they could grab, awoke to the nightmare that their city had become. Survivors simply dug through the rubble with their bare hands. It was four and a half hours before the city re-established contact with the outside world. And when the world found out, an extraordinary rescue operation got underway; within twenty-four hours there was a force of 10,000 digging through the rubble in search of life, and supplies began flying in from all over Europe.

For ten days Paul and his girlfriend stayed just outside the city in a make-shift camp organised by the British embassy. Then they were flown home. Paul not only lost his car, but he received no compensation, and had to go on paying back his loan for the next five years. The insurance company maintained that the earthquake had been an Act of God, and was therefore not covered in his policy. He didn't even have the broken steering wheel to show for it. In the course of trying to find survivors, it had somehow got lost. But he did not mind. Some travel experiences, he said, don't require souvenirs.

Paul never told us the name of the hotel that had saved his life on that night in July, 1963, but some forty years later I did not have to go far to find it. In fact, I didn't have to go anywhere at all. I had booked into the Bristol hotel knowing little about it, but when the taxi from the airport drew up in front of the six-storey building, I knew this was exactly where Paul's Austin Healey had perished. Either side of the hotel was an empty space where the other hotels must have stood. As I looked up at the second-floor windows, I imagined young Paul seeing the city reduced to ruins all around him, and looking across at the station, where, on the preserved, half-demolished façade, the clock still stands at seventeen minutes past five.

My room was on the top floor of this pleasant thirty-three-room hotel, and I now learned that the Bristol had been built between 1923 and 1924 for Atanas and Risto Karadza, traders from Skopje, as part of an ensemble of three hotels. The Bristol was used by *"trade agents and tourists to whom entertainment and company of pleasant dancing was offered"*. It was nationalised in 1947, and privatised in a management buyout in the 1990s. Its dining room was probably rather glamorous once, and its guests had apparently included Dame Rebecca West, though she does not mention the name of the hotel where she stayed in *Black Lamb and Grey Falcoln*, the book of her journeys through Yugoslavia. Without guide books, I don't suppose Paul Shepherd knew as much. In fact, he must have seen precious little of the city before it disappeared.

His story occupied a great deal of my thoughts as I walked around the town, whose hideous modern buildings can be forgiven in the light of the enormity of the disaster from which they had rapidly to grow. The city was not all ruined. On the far side of the old stone bridge the low-rise houses of the Turkish quarter were far less affected by the earthquake. Here, mosques and churches, *hammams* and *hans* survived. One magnificent han can still be seen with open fires in all the upstairs rooms.

Hotel Bristol apart, the buildings on Marshal Tito Street were all erected after 1963. The largest public monument in the street is to Mother Teresa. The house where she was born Agnes Gonxha Bojaxhiu to Nicola Bojaxhiu, an Albanian builder, and his wife, Dronda, in 1910 was an earthquake casualty. The city was undergoing great changes as she was growing up. She would have watched the Karadza brothers building the Bristol a few hundred yards away, and she would have seen the 300-year-old mosque by the old bridge being torn down to make way for the Habsburg-inspired Army Club, the dominant building in old postcards of the city, which are still on sale. The Ottomans had been defeated. The Christians were coming, and missionaries were flooding into the former Muslim empire, seeking recruits. Agnes was hooked and off she went, aged sixteen, first to Ireland, then to Calcutta.

Following independence in 1991, church and mosque building began again. In the violent break-up of Yugoslavia, the Republic of Macedonia had done rather well compared to its Balkan neighbours – Kosovo is just over the hills to the north, Albania to the west. Only a score of deaths on Macedonian soil can be attributed to the hostilities of the racial, political and religious mix that makes up the original macedoine. But its casualties were not unimportant, and Kiro Gligorov, the first president of the new Former Yugoslav Republic can be counted among them. When I met him at a cocktail party organised by some NGOs, he had been out of power for several years. In his early eighties, he was a personable enough, and was interested to hear what Maggie Thatcher had told me when I last met her – I had begun to use the Warsaw encounter with Matt to my advantage. As we talked, it was hard not to keep looking at the craters that scarred his forehead, which I presumed were the result of an assassination attempt in 1995 that had kept him incapacitated and out of office for a year.

He asked where I was staying and when I said the Bristol, his only remaining eyebrow, the right one, rose archly. There were far more modern hotels in the city, he said. I didn't want to get into a long story about my father's friend and the earthquake, so I simply mentioned my eccentric interest in all things Bristol. Usually this brings some light-hearted comments but Gligorov did not seem amused. He simply scowled in incomprehension before moving away to find a more interesting person to speak to. Shortly afterwards, he left. I hoped I had not upset the former president by my admission that I was staying in the modest Bristol, when I could have been spending at least twice as many Macedonian kruns in a smarter place and I said as much to Sava, one of my hosts.

"You don't know about the assassination attempt on the president?" He was a serious, well educated young man and his English was precise.

"Not in any detail."

One side of Sava's mouth smiled as he handed me a canapé. "The president was driving in his motorcade by the old railway station when the car bomb went off. His chauffeur, Aleksander Spirkovski, a good man, was killed, and a dozen passers by were badly injured. Something like twenty kilos of explosives had been put in the back of a Citroën Ami 8, which was parked outside the Hotel Bristol. The car had also been filled with bags of sand so that the force was directed out across the road, to make a cushion with the hotel."

"The Bristol?"

"So it is not surprising he has bad memories of the place."

No indeed.

I thought of Paul Shepherd and his words of wisdom, about always being able to find a hotel near a railway station. Now I was able to offer further advice.

If anyone were ever to ask me for my top tip about travelling it would be this: *Never leave your car parked outside a Hotel Bristol.*

15: LELAND STANFORD AND STENDHAL'S SYNDROME

Helvetia & Bristol
Florence, Italy
www.royaldemeure.com

When she collapsed, the woman wasn't staring at *The Birth of Venus*, as everyone later believed. She had been caught up in the Botticelli bottleneck of the Uffizzi Gallery's Room 14 when her knees suddenly became useless and she crumpled like a sack of potatoes dumped off a truck. I watched her go. Her head hit the wood floor with such a smack that people winced and stepped back to stare at her as if she were a piece of installation art on which they suddenly had to have an opinion. Her companion, whom I took to be an old friend, was immediately at her side, dropping down on the floor and calling out her name, though it was hard to see what was happening in the midst of the crowd. In a few moments a couple of curators cleared a path and I was able to glimpse the tableau of one woman cradled in the arms of another, a *pietà vivant*.

Collapsing in public is never dignified and the older and more respectable you are, the greater the downfall seems to be. The victim was aged around sixty, on the heavy side, her loose hair streaked to look like the genuine article bleached by the Italian sun. The linen and raw cotton materials now awkwardly arranged around her were not cheaply bought, nor were her shoes or handbag that had spilled its contents across the floor. You would not expect anything less than money and good taste from a woman staying at the five-star Helvetia & Bristol in Florence, the only Bristol in the world to have an entry in Herbert Ypma's Hip Hotel series. The woman's name was Dora, her companion was called Connie and they were about my mother's age. I knew their names and that they were from California, because I had overheard them that morning at breakfast on the hotel terrace, when they were a couple of tables away from mine.

I can't remember ever seeing smelling salts in action before, but a curator uncorked a small, dark bottle and placed it beneath Dora's nostrils. In a few minutes she came round. However, the crack that her head had received apparently made the fainting fit potentially rather more serious than it might otherwise have been, and the sound of an ambulance was soon wailing in the heavy June heat outside the Palazzo Vecchio.

Among the mutterings of the people in the room, I heard the words "Stendhal's Syndrome" mentioned several times and I was not surprised. This condition, which is named after the 19th-century French writer who became physically affected by the art of Florence, is supposed to strike the occasional visitor still, but I was sure that the American woman was not a victim of Stendhal's or anybody else's Syndrome. She could not have been. She had not been looking at any painting when she collapsed. Her gaze had just fallen on a man of around twenty who had entered the room from the East Gallery. In his early twenties with darting black eyes and olive skin, his unmistakable Italian looks were confirmed by his stylish white shirt and cropped blue cargo shorts. His female companion was equally attractive and relaxed. Though Dora had caught sight of him, he had not noticed her, and even after she had fallen I saw that he did not give her more than a passing glance, raising his eyebrows and shrugging to his companion before moving away into the next room. Yet when Dora had seen him, in that fraction of a second before she hit the floor, her whole face contorted, her jaw dropped, her pale eyes bulged and colour drained from her.

But all this was nothing to do with me. After reassuring myself that there wasn't anything useful that I could do, I moved on, heading down the corridor and only briefly visiting the remaining rooms. I was by now starting to become sated with art and was mentally ticking off canvases the way that some students were physically checking them against their course-work lists. So many extraordinary paintings were hard to digest and though I was not about to swoon *alla* Stendhal, I was soon happy to find myself in the last room where reassuring neoclassical portraits were less troublesome to the spirit.

One untroubled painter was François-Xavier Fabre, whom the Earl-Bishop Bristol introduced to the Countess Albany in Florence in 1793. The painting she sat for that same year, when she was forty-one, was hanging here in Room 45. Not long after their introduction, the young painter began to live in a *ménage à trois* with the Countess and the Italian poet Count Vittorio Alfieri. Critics have described the German-born Countess as odious and ugly, and though Fabre failed to soften her harsh features I would not care to pass any judgment on the strength of a painting. Her Florentine salons were famous and she inspired jealousy in her lovers. She thought Bristol a fool, which may be the reason why he failed to set his cap, or mitre, at her, but she could not have been devoid of attraction. Yet her mouth is not soft and there is a weariness in her eyes. Perhaps she was bitter. Her husband, Charles Edward Stuart, son of James II and pretender to the English and Scottish thrones, was by then dead. Bonnie Prince Charlie had been a drunk and a wife beater and she had failed to provide him with an heir. Perhaps it was just as well, as he may well have turned out to be as discontented and bitter as his father.

John Augustus, Lord Hervey, son and heir of the Earl-Bishop, inherited the family tradition of courting trouble. Though a hot-head lacking his father's charm, in 1787 he was appointed British Minister to the Count of Tuscany in Florence. At first it was just his private life that caused a stir, not least when he disgraced himself with his unwanted advances towards Lady Webster, a pivotal figure on the local social scene. "*He proceeded to downright violence,*" she recorded. "*Oh what vile animals men are.*"

It was his insults to the Grand Duke that caused his eventual removal, however. One reason for Lord Hervey's rudeness towards the Grand Duke was annoyance at Tuscany's refusal to break off its commercial ties with revolutionary France, where massacre and pillage were raging. Napoleon Bonapart's Armée d'Italie successfully negotiated the Alpine passes and began advancing across Italy in April 1796. But Lord Hervey never lived to see it, or to feel himself vindicated. He had died of fever at sea a few months earlier. His father, ill in Naples, was "*bouleversée*". Politics in Europe were explosive, rumours everywhere were rife, and Bristol could not be kept to a sick bed for long. Soon he was heading north, insatiable for news. The French by now were heading south. They had defeated the Austrians in Piedmont and created the Cisalpine Republic, with its capital at Milan. Bristol picked up what gossip and information he could, sending off letters to Berlin, London and Naples, where Queen Maria Carolina, sister of the lately beheaded Marie Antoinette, was particularly anxious to learn of developments. Eventually, in February 1798, travelling from Venice to Rome, Bristol was arrested and held for nine months in the Castello Sforzesco in Milan. Writing to Britain's Foreign Secretary, Lord Grenville, Sir William Hamilton said, "*We know that his lordship's freedom of conversation, particularly after dinner, is such as to make him liable to accidents of this nature.*"

I had just come from Milan, where the previous week I had been staying at the excellent four-star Bristol next to the railway station. A firm of Japanese trophy-hunters had acquired a large and successful furniture designers with my help, and I was just tying up loose ends. I had hoped to visit Castello Sforzesco, which is now a series of museums and galleries, to tread the floorboards and stone corridors that for nine months had been paced by the imprisoned Earl-Bishop. Work, however, did not allow me any free time during opening hours, so the visit had to be postponed.

Now I was in Florence on my own. Sophie should have been with me. I had booked a weekend in the Helvetia & Bristol on a whim. Neither of us had been to Florence before, and Sophie should have flown out to join me. But at the last minute her work got in the way, and she had to stay behind. She urged me to carry on with my plans, as she would be no fun, stuck in front of a computer. I had to concur. Weekends at home when one of us was working were invariably a sullen mixture of irritation and rejection.

One advantage of being alone is that art galleries can be easier to visit. Sophie is far more assiduous than I am, reading every caption, staring at every mark on a canvas, and I end up hanging around by the exit, wandering back and forth, estimating visitor numbers and museum profits or checking out the café facilities and shopping opportunities. If she had been with me now, I'm not sure she would have completed the tour of the gallery before it closed, let alone the Palazzo Pitti, which was included in the price of the ticket. Lord Bristol never met a Medici but he would have seen many of these art treasures. The last of the dynasty had died in the 1750s and the estate was bequeathed to the people of Florence. The Uffizzi, the offices, which adjoined the old palace, became a public gallery. A first-floor thoroughfare that joins these buildings to the Palazzo Pitti Palace, the other Medici stronghold on the other side of the River Arno, crossing via the upper storey of the Ponte Vecchio, was closed, so after I had finished ruminating on Countess Albany I wandered out into the hot, dry June afternoon, carrying my linen jacket that was too warm to wear. After buying a straw hat and an ice cream I strolled over the bridge. The gold and silver trinkets on sale in the tiny shops on the Ponte Vecchio were way overpriced, but it didn't matter. I picked out a silver bracelet for Sophie, just so I could say I had bought it there.

After a tour of the Pitti Palace I went and sat in the shade of the Cypresses in Bobilo Gardens and gave her a call.

"Hello?" she said.

"Hello, it's me."

"I thought it would be you."

"How's work?"

"Getting there. How's Florence?"

"Hot, crowded, full of art."

To make her feel less bad at being cooped up on the weekend that she should have been sight-seeing in the sun, I told her how hard it was to see some of the paintings because of the crush. And I went on to describe the drama in the Uffizzi's Room 14, explaining the theory of Stendhal's Syndrome,. No fewer than seven Florentine artworks, including Michelangelo's David, were said to be particularly prone to producing this effect.

"How wonderful," she said, "to see a something that makes you swoon."

"Well you should see me now," I said, because at that moment the young Italian couple that the American woman had spotted when she fainted walked by and I had an inspired idea. "*Prego*," I called out, pointing the instrument towards them. They turned towards me with polite curiosity. "My girlfriend is on the phone from London. She wants a picture of me in front of the Pitti Palace. Would you mind?"

Of course, they would not mind at all. I handed over my phone and explained what to press to take a picture. Then I put on my hat at a rakish angle, hung my jacket on my shoulders like a native and stepped out into the sunshine in front of the palace, lifting my head so that my face would not be too much in the shadow of the straw brim.

"Say 'Leonardo'!" the Italian called as he pressed the button.

By the time I had returned to his side, the young man had the phone to his ear and was saying hello to Sophie, introducing himself as Mario Fantoni from Bergamo and telling her that she had a very nice boyfriend and it was a very nice day and asking her where was it that she lived in England. He had been to London once. Madame Tussauds, London Eye. It was very nice.

A thousand miles away, Sophie listened patiently to this charade. A picture of me in the Boboli Ga rdens would not make her blink, let alone swoon, but now was not the time to explain what I was up to; I would do that on my return. The next step was to take a picture of Mario Fantoni and his girlfriend, who was called Francesca, so that Sophie could see who she had been talking to – or that was the excuse I gave. I asked for his email address and promised to send the pictures to him, too.

Feeling pleased with myself, I returned to the hotel an hour or so later. I was more than ready to put my feet up and get the most from my elegant room before venturing on to the streets again. The Helvetia & Bristol was in the grand hotel manner, built in the 19th century to attract English visitors. According to Herb Ypma's eulogy, it is close to the benchmark of E. M. Forster's *Room with a View*. It has around fifty rooms with a couple of fifth-floor suites overlooking Brunaleschi's dome and each room is handsomely furnished, plumped up in silk, damask and brocaded wallpaper with real antiques, period prints and paintings. It was a fitting place to stay in this city of culture and high art.

Before going to my room, I wanted to discover if the hotel had any printing facilities for my digital pictures, but Dora, the American, was already at the oak-panelled desk in the narrow lobby in conversation with the receptionist. She was going to wait until the following day before deciding whether to stay another night, and she wanted to know if her room could still be available. Her manner was direct and her blue eyes were locked on the receptionist. High cheek bones must have made her quite striking a few decades ago. The California sun had given her a healthy glow and any lines it might naturally have produced had been nipped and tucked out of sight so that her skin seemed as if it had been ironed. She was almost my height, her short hair naturally fair, almost white. Scandinavia may have figured somewhere in her family's past.

While the receptionist checked the room availability, I asked after her companion, explaining that I had been in the Uffizzi's Room 14 when the drama had occurred.

"They're keeping her in for observation," she said, turning her full attention on me. "They tried to tell me it was something called Stendhal's Syndrome, which you're supposed to get when you OD on art. I never heard so much hooey. I had to insist they checked her out properly. The first my mother knew she had cancer was when she fainted in a mall."

I asked if their plans had been upset by the incident and she said that a car due to take them to Venice the next morning had to be cancelled and the company didn't want to reimburse her. When I pointed out that her travel insurance would pay for it, she looked doubtful. I assured her that the policy should cover not only the cancelled car but any other extra expense, too, such as additional nights at the Helvetia & Bristol. She brightened.

"I'll call them." She looked at her watch. "It's only lunchtime back home. Venice we can do another day."

"Are you often in Italy?"

"First time for both of us."

The receptionist had by now put a hold on a room for another night, and Dora wanted to know when dinner was served in the restaurant. When she was told any time after seven o'clock, she said that she would be there on the button, and asked for a taxi to be ordered to take her back to the hospital at eight. She didn't want to stray far from a phone.

I don't usually like to eat early, but an ice cream and a couple of cappuccinos were all I had got around to since breakfast. It was still stifling outside and air conditioning could only improve an appetite. The hotel restaurant looked interesting. Its walls, upholstery, drapes were all deep burgundy, the small round white tables scattered about beneath strange grotto chandeliers, and the menu was Tuscan and tempting.

I was already sitting at a corner table, reading Vasari's *Lives*, when Dora walked in. An envelope containing a print of my mobile phone's photograph of Mario Fantoni was on the damask tablecloth by my right hand, ready to be pulled out at the right moment, when I would ask why the sight of this young man could have had such a devastating effect on her friend. By now my money was Mario turning out to be a long-lost relative, perhaps even a son.

Though on her own, Dora was dressed as if she were on her way to a social function, in a peach-coloured suit, silk blouse and heels. Nobody else was interested in eating at that hour, and as the only diner in the room, I stood up to greet her, inviting her to join me. She looked relieved and sat down, her chair manoeuvred into the exact spot by a discreet waiter. The handbag she placed at her feet was soft Italian leather and the diamond on the thin silver choker at her throat was real. So was the cluster on her wedding ring. She may have never been to Italy before but she had clearly been around.

We introduced ourselves. After thanking me for the advice about her insurance, which had proved fruitful, we had a discussion about the menu. She wanted to try something with truffles but it wasn't the season, so she settled for a *bisteca alla fiorentina* and I chose a pigeon risotto. She did not want any wine with her meal, so we had mineral water and it wasn't long before her story came tumbling out.

Dora and Connie had met at Stanford University in California back in the 1960s. They had both studied art, and they had always promised they would make a trip to Europe. Stanford University, she pointed out, had a connection with Florence. I had seen the plaque on the side of our hotel. Leland Stanford, Governor of California (1861–63), was a rail baron with powerful energy and a range if interests. As president of the Central Pacific Railroad Company he had picked up a hammer made of Nevada silver and driven the last spike, fashioned out of California gold, into the final section of the transcontinental railway across the Sierra Nevada, linking the East coast with the West. In California he owned the largest vineyard in the world and a trotting horse stud farm called Palo Alto. His fascination with both science and the arts led him to commission the photographer Eadweard Muybridge to set up a series of photographs triggered by trip wires to prove that all four legs of a horse left the ground when it galloped.

Stanford and his wife Jane, the daughter of a New York

merchant, had only one child, who was also called Leland. The boy inherited his father's curiosity and intelligence, his mother's too, and enjoyed all the considerable benefits that his family had to offer. But in 1884, on a trip to Europe, he contracted typhoid fever. Perhaps it had been when he was steering a boat on the Bosphorous, or when he had had been in Athens, where he met the German archaeologist Heinrich Schliemann, who had just discovered the city of Troy. As the boy's health deteriorated in the first weeks of the year, the Stanfords were persuaded that the climate in Florence would be beneficial. So they booked into the Bristol Hotel.

Here, for three weeks Leland Jr lay in a feverish state, nursed by nuns and attended by physicians who wrapped him in icy blankets to try to bring his temperature down. The hotel manager ordered straw to be spread on the street outside to deaden the sound of the horses. But on March 30 he died. It was two months before his 16th birthday, just before his studies at Harvard were to begin. His father had been at his bedside in the Bristol Hotel suite throughout the brief illness and he is reported to have woken from a dream after the boy died and turned to his wife Jane and said, "The children of California shall be our children."

And so, exactly a year after their son's death, the cornerstone of the Leland Stanford Jr University was laid in part of the Palo Alto farm.

Doris made the Stanfords sound like personal friends, and when she came to the end of the story, I commiserated with her. Losing a child must be the worst thing in the world. My right hand pressed on the envelope containing the photograph I had taken of Mario Fantoni. *Whose son was he?*

"What about you and your friend Connie?" I asked. "Do you have children?"

"I'm blessed with two grown children and three of beautiful grandchildren." Doris took a picture from her purse of two girls and a boy, pointing to each in turn and giving their names and ages. They looked healthy, sunny, Californian.

"And Connie?" I asked after giving them what I thought was sufficient praise. By now I was itching to show my own photograph.

"She never had any. Her marriage didn't last long."

"No children?" I hoped I did not sound too disappointed. I was sure I had been on the right track. Taking my hand from the envelope, I broke some bread and chewed it for a moment, wondering why else just the sight of Mario Fantoni would have made Connie faint. "And you waited all this time to make your European trip together?"

"Not exactly. We came over in 1968, just after we graduated."

"I thought you said you had never been to Italy before."

"We didn't get this far. We were in Paris when Connie had some bad news and we headed straight home."

At that moment the food arrived and we were diverted into commenting on the plates set before us. I was impatient to know more but I did not press the point until a couple of forkfuls of risotto had gone down and we had passed appraisal on our choices.

"Her beau from University had been killed in Vietnam," Dora finally said. "She took a long time to get over it."

"I'm sorry." I tried to calculate how old a love child might be.

She gave a small sigh. Though she was still looking at me in that intense way, her eyes were a little dreamy now. "She took it very badly. We all did, he was a popular guy, and very handsome in a dark, Mediterranean way. Something special. Such a waste." She shook her head.

"She married somebody else in the end?"

"A disaster. 'My big booboo' is how she refers to her ex-husband now. A major mistake."

"What was he like?"

"I never met him, and I don't think I would have wanted to. He beat up on her, she says. But I didn't know her then. We lost touch when I got married not long after Mario was killed. It was only after my husband died last year that we reconnected. It was

Connie's idea that we picked up where we left off forty years ago. We've just come from Paris."

"Mario? Did you say that was her beau's name?"

"Yes, he was from an Italian family. The Fantonis. As a matter of fact, they originally came from near here, from a place called Bergamo."

"Mario Fantoni… from Bergamo…" I slid the envelope from the table and pushed it into my pocket. I didn't want to show her the photograph now, in case she, too, was overcome with Stendhal's Syndrome.

"You've gone mighty pale," she said. "I hope you aren't going to faint."

146

16: THE LONELY DOLL
AND THE CASTOR OIL KING

**Radio City Apartments
New York, USA
www.radiocityapartments.com**

I found out by chance that Sophie was staying at the Radio City Apartments on West 49th Street where her boss maintained a two-room pied-à-terre. She had been vague about where she would be in New York, and I hadn't pressed her to leave an address. I was submerged beneath a hefty work load and I imagined keeping in touch by email, so her actual whereabouts hadn't seemed important. You could say it was my fault for being inattentive. It was only some weeks later, when a friend of hers let go a remark, that I realised Sophie and Patrick Hammer had shared the apartment alone for the best part of a week.

"It was all quite proper." Hurt surfaced in Sophie's perfectly made-up eyes as she spoke, the long lashes working overtime. "But I never told you because I knew you'd get the wrong idea."

Private detectives are an old-fashioned concept, but sometimes, when the green-eyed monster raises its head, the thought of hiring a disinterested third party to find out exactly what the hell is going on becomes appealing.

In the spring of 1949 a private investigator famously paid a visit to the building now occupied by the Radio City Apartments. In those days this was the grand, 145-room brownstone Bristol Hotel, one of the hottest places in Manhattan. Dick Longman was the private investigator employed to discover the nature of the antics, if such they were, that were taking place in Room 512. Longman was not a born snoop, but he was no greenhorn either, and he had been earning a steady income from his office in Queens since being demobbed four years earlier. As a wartime foot soldier he had gained no more than a corporal's stripes in the slog across Europe from Normandy to Berlin, an experience he was reluctant to recall. On his return to New York at the age of twenty-nine, he had discovered that his widowed mother, instead of welcoming him home, had died, leaving all her money to his unpleasant sister, while his wife, Adele, had found comfort in the arms of a fellow, female munitions worker. On the whole, these two events made him feel rejected by women, but after several years in the services, he hadn't taken much to men, either.

For a while, he held no torches for women and he felt unable to look them in the eye, but he had no trouble noticing their legs. The pavements of New York were full of them. In fact he believed them to be the most welcoming aspect of his return to civilisation. In silken stockings striding beneath the flounce of increasingly generous skirts, clacking their high heels on the kerbs, they had a sense of freedom and individual purpose that his couple of years in gaiters and rough serge had lacked. They were one reason he took up detective work, specialising in divorce. The weeping of betrayed clients would frequently be accompanied by the frisson of silken nylon, as legs were crossed and uncrossed in fury and despair, while his popping flashlight was likely to snap souvenir pictures of wives or mistresses with no stockings on at all.

The army had instilled in Longman a sense of order that continued to drive him from his bed early every day and kept his shoes shining, his shirts clean, and banished all but essential creases in his grey nylon suits. A need for order and an appreciation of women's legs was a combination that was bound to drive him sooner or later into the Radio City Music Hall where the Rockettes, the famous high-kicking dancing troupe, performed four times a day seven days a week. They were a complete revelation to him, a marvel, a heaven, particularly when they high-kicked their way through a routine called Parade of the Wooden Soldiers. As often as he could, Longman bought a ticket and a tub of popcorn to sit back and watch this sensational spectacle.

Soon he was a stage-door Johnnie and more. Using detective

skills, which incorporated a certain amount of guile, it was only a matter of weeks before he was dating Flora Pidgin, who at 5ft 10in stood near the centre of the chorus line of three dozen Rockettes most days of the week. Her hair was pale and her face was packed with make-up, covering skin that suffered from a lack of daylight and a constant layering of greasepaint. Longman, himself no Clark Gable, thought her exotic from head to toe.

"You're the first woman in three years I've been able to look fully in the eye," he said as they stood at the cocktail bar on their first date. In her heels she had an inch over him.

"I hope you're not going to talk about women who have let you down," she said. "There's nothing more boring."

"I won't even talk about my dead mother," he promised. "From now on life will be nothing but a ball."

"I'll drink to that," Flora said.

Flora's room mate and fellow Rockette was Tilley Johnson, another piece of talent on two legs from Fargo, North Dakota, who was about an inch shorter than Flora. She was dating Billy Veit, a large man a few years older than Longman, whose lack of charm was countered by a generous wallet and a thirst he did not like to quench alone. On occasion, they would make up a foursome and hit some clubs and bars, like the Pink Elephant in the Hotel Bristol across from Radio City Hall, where they liked to sample the cocktails. Several times they went for a ride in Billy's powder-blue Cadillac Club coupé, and he promised to take them on a picnic to Long Island some day. On the sweet smelling leather back seat with Flora, Longman was sure it would be only a matter of time before he himself was behind the wheel of a similar automobile.

"Tilley got an executive, and all I got was a gumshoe," Flora teased. "Where did I go wrong?"

"I'll have a fleet of cars for you one day, sugar." Longman squeezed her thigh. "One for each day of the week, and one left over in case the upholstery tones clash with the outfit you happen to have chosen to wear."

"I like that idea," Flora said.

What Billy Veit was an executive of, no one quite knew, and though he often talked about "the office" and kept a pocket full of dimes for frequent phone calls, he never seemed to work late and he was always available for daytime expeditions. He became a regular at the Pink Elephant Bar and the management was always pleased to see his friends, too. When Billy told the head barman he should be giving them drinks on the house for prettying up the place with a couple of high-kickers who had to be good for trade, he did not make the proposition lightly.

All four of them were at a table in the Pink Elephant one night just after New Year when Billy's younger sister, Mary, came by with her husband, a rotund, middle-aged man in tweeds with thick sandy eyebrows and tufts of hair in his ears, who made Longman think of a brown bear.

"This is my sister Mary and my dear brother-in-law Fenimore Cooper Marsh," Billy said by way of introductions. "We call him Coop. Be nice to him because he is an oil tycoon."

"Oh, I love oil tycoons," Tilley said extending her hand.

"I must warn you against such generosity of spirit." Fenimore Cooper Marsh shook the hand lightly. "Some tycoons I've met are not real gentlemen."

"Oh?" said Tilley "I find that so hard to believe."

Longman said, "Allow me to buy the drinks."

While the detective was up at the bar, a striking blonde came up to their table and greeted Mary like an old friend. With a finely chiselled face and a nose that swept up at the last moment, she might have been a model or a society woman, though her white taffeta dress, a mix of bridal gown and house coat, set off by her vermilion nails and lips, made her look more like a child who had been at the dressing up box.

"Who's the doll, Mary?" Billy said as Marsh pulled up a chair for the woman to join them.

"This is my big brother Billy and his friends Tilly and Flora," Mary said to the woman. "Billy, this is Dare Wright. She lives in a suite here in the Bristol and she takes photographs."

"Dare Wright?" Billy feigned a look of surprise. "What d'you *dare write*, Dare Wright? '*Kilroy was here*'?"

Billy liked this joke, and his sister did, too. It cracked them up. But the blonde didn't even seem to have heard it, so he repeated what he had said.

"Dare Wright is my name," she said. "Mary, I thought you might like to see the dark room I've rigged up in my room."

"A dark room? How interesting." Fenimore Cooper's doleful eyes brightened. "We sure would, wouldn't we, Mary? I have always been so fascinated by the art of photography."

"What you going to *dare write* in the dark room? '*Will somebody please put the fuckin' lights on*?' " Billy enjoyed this joke even more than his first one.

Dare Wright seemed puzzled. "There would be no point. Nobody could read it."

After the Marshes had left, Billy started to get a little loud. He had made no impression on the blonde, and this irked him, so he began putting her down, calling her a stuck-up bitch and so forth. Tilley told him to mind his language, and Longman made an excuse of an early morning set-up to leave early with Flora. His landlady, a retired psychic, usually knew what he was up to and didn't like him getting in too late.

Billy was frequently in the Pink Elephant at the Bristol after that. Longman dropped in now and then, too, in the hope of making some society contacts, but he and Flora preferred to do their dallying elsewhere. Finally, after a number of reminders from Tilley, Billy Veit fired up the Cadillac and took them all on an outing to Long Island. It was so cold they did not wish to remove their coats and hats when they settled on the beach with a picnic hamper of cold chicken and beer. In the summertime, Billy told them, Dare Wright and her mother sunbathed naked on the beach and took photographs of one another. Or so his sister said. Longman thought of his ex-wife, Adele, and her girlfriend and wondered if they ever sunbathed nude on the beach.

"Mothers and daughters are always close," Flora pointed out.

"It ain't natural," Billy said.

"Buff ain't natural?" said Tilley.

"Not with your mother."

"I suppose it's okay with the bell hop."

Billy shrugged. "Well, yeah. That's more like natural."

Billy didn't have anything pleasant to say about Dare Wright. She modelled brassieres for the magazines, he said, and her mother was a pushy socialite portrait painter from Cincinatti. Dare wore some of the weirdest clothes. In his own mind Longman associated her with Adele: a woman who had no need of men.

"I don't know what goes on up in her room in that hotel, with its photo laboratory and all," Billy said, "but I sure as hell would like to know. Wouldn't surprise me if she was on the game, and maybe with Fenimore, too. I've seen him going up in the hotel lift on more than one occasion."

It wasn't so much of a surprise, therefore, when a few weeks later Longman got a call at his office from Billy to say that he and his sister wanted to see him on a matter of urgent business. Shortly afterwards the powder-blue Cadillac drew up outside the detective's office, watched by Longman from his first-floor window. Mary Marsh was driving and Billy was in the passenger seat.

Dressed dramatically in black, the oil millionaire's wife swept into the office and sat down. "I'll come straight to the point," she said. "I believe my husband is having an affair with Dare Wright in Room 512 of the Hotel Bristol. All I need is a little confirmation of this delicate matter."

"Have you talked to Miss Wright?" Longman asked.

"What would be the point of that?" Billy said.

"I thought she was a good friend of mine," Mary's angry voice was harsh. "Last Christmas I bought Coop an expensive tripod because of his interest in photography. Yesterday I noticed it had gone missing."

"He gave it to the broad," Billy said. "I saw him carry it into the hotel lift. It's not an implement you might mistake for something else, such as an umbrella."

Longman could see that this was a straightforward case. He sat back and asked about Marsh's habits, his routines, how often he visited the hotel, where he ate and drank. Mary gave him her visiting card, but told him not to get in touch directly.

"We have children," she said. "I don't want them hurt."

"You're dealing with me here, Mr Detective" said Billy. "I'm the go-between."

"Oil millionaire, is he?" Longman stared at the card with the Park Avenue address, trying to get the full picture.

"Castor oil," said Billy. "Bakers Castor Oil of New Jersey, the biggest castor oil manufacturer in the world. Marsh is the Castor Oil King."

Longman tried hard not to smile. He could see a down payment on a Cadillac coming up, and he couldn't wait to tell Flora. Sitting back, he looked Mary Veit in the eye.

"In a case like this," he said, "to make sure we spring our trap at precisely the right moment, I would generally employ a psychic, a reliable practitioner that we regularly use. Ruth Mason cut her teeth with Harry Houdini who liked to have her on hand because he knew that however deep the water he got into she would know immediately if anything was about to go fatally wrong. Houdini himself believed that she saved his life on a couple of occasions."

Billy whistled. "Sounds like a handy lady to have around."

Longman's clients always liked this Houdini angle. And if the Castor Oil King was going to bankroll this raid, it was time to start throwing money around. Besides, Rose was his landlady, and he liked to keep in with her.

"Miss Mason will be able to confirm when the moment is hot. So what I'll need from you, Mrs Marsh is a some item of your husband's that she can communicate through, like one of his old handkerchiefs, or a sock."

She stood up to leave. "You can have his whole damned wardrobe as far as I'm concerned."

It took little more than a week to stake out the hotel. Mary Marsh paid for a room to be rented on the same floor in the adjoining corridor, where Longman could make a note of who came and went from Dare Wright's room. Billy abandoned any pretence of going to his "office" and spent nearly all his waking hours on the case around Radio City Hall opposite, keeping an eye on the hotel entrance and the offending party's fifth-floor window. He was as anxious for quick results as his sister, who kept him informed of her husband's movements, warning when she thought a visit to the Bristol was imminent. The millionaire appeared to have no idea that anything untoward was going on, and when he arrived at the hotel he never tried to hide himself in any way. His chauffeur-driven Pontiac would drive right up outside to be greeted by the gold-braided doorman. On the first occasion, Billy noted, Marsh was carrying a grocery bag, which he did not possess when he left. The second time he stayed until nearly 11pm, and the lights in the apartment went out on several occasions.

Those two visits were, Longman believed, more than enough evidence to justify a raid.

The planning centred on Ruth Mason, Longman's psychic landlady. Though gone sixty and no bigger than a bird, she believed her powers to be stronger than ever. Longman took her to the hotel room at 6pm on the last Thursday in May, where she sat in a button-back leather armchair stroking a tartan sock that belonged to Marsh. Mary and Billy arrived shortly after with their younger brother, Duke, an overweight, taciturn man who had been recruited as a further witness and for his additional poundage. From the start, Longman realised that there would be no way of keeping the family out of this job, and all he could do now was hope they didn't screw up.

"We don't pussy-foot with this one." Longman stood by the window to address his squad. "No knocking on the door and pretending to be Western Union with a telegram, or room service with Champagne. We wait till the tycoon is settled down with the dame, and when Miss Mason here senses that they're up to no good, we bust the place. I'm talking splintered hardwood here. A big noise. *Ker-bam!*" He smacked a fist into a palm. "Billy, you and Duke are going to have to get us into that room with one flying blockbuster. We'll pay for the damage. It's nothing of nothing percent compared to what that philandering phoney is going to cough up."

"What are you doing all this time?" Billy wanted to know.

"I'm right behind you. Once you're in the room, you let me through fast. I come in with the camera popping. Don't get in my way. Keep your eyes open. We all make statements with the lawyers tomorrow and they'll want to know everything we saw. First, though, we'll meet in my office at nine o'clock and pool all our knowledge, make sure we all saw the same things."

Ruth began to rub the sock with both hands. "Mr Marsh is just arriving."

Longman flicked back the lace curtain. "Yuh-huh. Spot on as usual, Miss Mason."

"This has to go right," Mary Marsh said. "It's not the kind of thing you can do twice."

"You stay in this room, Mrs Marsh." Longman picked up his camera. "Wait by the phone. The second I have finished taking my pictures we'll leave, and we'll call you from the street. There's no need for you to be involved in the actual act of discovery. It could be an upsetting occasion for you. Miss Mason here will stay with you till we're all done."

Half an hour after Fenimore Cooper Marsh entered the Hotel Bristol, Ruth Mason stood up quietly, dropping the sock and wiping her hands on a handkerchief. She sniffed the air like a dog on a scent. "Gentlemen," she said, "the occupants of room 512 have become aroused."

Without a word, the three men tiptoed off down the corridor, hoping no one would be passing. Longman put first his ear to the door of 512, then his eye to the keyhole. Inside, the light went out. He took a step sideways. The Veit brothers put their backs to the wall opposite. Longman nodded. They rushed the door. It exploded on impact. Longman leapt into action, swinging his camera in through the splintered wreckage, nearly tripping over Billy who had fallen to the floor. The couple emerged from the bathroom. Flashbulbs popped, illuminating their surprise. The lights came on and Fenimore Cooper Marsh roared his outrage.

The tycoon and Dare Wright had not been caught *in flagrante delicto*, but this was good enough. His jacket was on the back of a chair and his tie was loosened. She was wearing a white gown tied with a bright sash, and when the camera bulbs popped, the light bounced off a mirror revealing the outline of her legs beneath. It also lit the glass eyes of a doll propped on the bed, giving Longman a momentary feeling that someone was catching him out, too.

"I'm Dick Longman, Private Detective," Longman said when his bulbs had run out. "And I must warn you that what we have witnessed here tonight will be the cause of a court case in which your wife will be obliged to sue for divorce."

"I know you, boy," Marsh said with menace, though he was still rooted to the spot.

"No threats now, Mr Marsh. Your in-laws are witnesses. We'll see you in court."

Dare Wright looked completely bemused, managing to raise only an eyebrow. "Goodness," she said, and without any fuss she sat down on the bed.

Longman ushered the brothers from the room and left the building right away, jumping into a cab to take him back to his office to develop the film, and leaving Billy to call his sister to tell her of their success.

Billy made some other calls, too. By the following day the story was splashed all over the papers. CASTOR OIL KING CAUGHT CANOODLING... TYCOON IN HOTEL TRYST... REGULAR MEETINGS... LOVE NEST AT THE BRISTOL... BLONDE SNAPPER SNAPPED... WIFE DEVASTATED... COUPLE SPLIT... WIFE AND KIDS MOVE OUT OF PARK AVENUE HOME... WRONGED WOMAN DEMANDS $3,000 A WEEK ALIMONY.

"You really nailed them." Flora said over cocktails a long way from the Pink Elephant.

"More important," said Longman, "with the bonus Mrs Marsh has promised when the court case is over, we'll be driving up to Long Island for picnics all summer long. And this time you and I will be in the front seats."

She kissed him impulsively, leaving a red smear on his cheek. "Didn't I say how much I love oil tycoons?"

"It's castor oil, sugar. That's the kind of mess he's in."

But the case took all summer to resolve. The preliminary hearings came up at the New York Supreme Court in July, and the accused took the stand. Dare Wright described herself as a portrait photographer specialising in children, which made Billy snort in derision, causing the District Attorney to cast an angry eye in his direction. She had been a friend of Mary Marsh and her children, she said, and they had often lunched together. She had known of Mr Marsh's interest in photography and it was only with Mary's encouragement that he had volunteered to help in the construction of a dark room in the hotel bathroom. Of course the lights were constantly switched off. She was cool, detatched, as if the charges had nothing to do with her. Her hotel room had been like that, Longman reflected: decorated in red and white striped cloths in a fancy, controlled way. Catching her eye, he recalled the doll on the counterpane, looking right back at him, and he turned away.

Longman felt no sympathy for Wright. A single woman didn't entertain a married man in her room, especially not a father with children. If photography was her business, why didn't she do it in business hours? It was certainly an expensive business and this woman was not rich. At thirty-five, it turned out, she had never been married and her work didn't sound as if it was particularly regular. Her mother was in court, dolled up like her daughter. Maybe she was in on the plan to bag a millionaire.

Fenimore Cooper Marsh took the stand looking pale, his brown bear locks and moustache neatly trimmed. "I told my wife each time I was going to the Hotel Bristol," he said in reply to the questioning. "And the children knew, too. It was no secret. Mary and Dare have been friends a while now, and my interest in photography is well known."

Asked if he had been having any marital problems he thought a moment before he said, "Well, I guess my wife just doesn't like me..." he paused and looked towards her, but she turned her head away... "as much as she likes my money."

For a few days the papers reported the case of the blonde photographer and the Castor Oil King. There were pictures of them dodging questions between the courthouse and their cars. Longman remained in the shadows.

His turn to testify did not come until the full trial in December. The court room was packed. When he took the stand he described in some detail the scene that had greeted him on that night back in March: how the lights went on and off, how the couple appeared from the bathroom in a state of undress, that brown bear fur of Marsh's pushing up from the top of his vest beneath the shirt he had been hurriedly buttoning as he pulled on his tie.

"Would you describe Miss Wright's garment as diaphanous?" the council for the plaintive asked.

"I don't know about materials and what they're called. It looked like some sort of cotton to me,"

"I mean, could you see through it?"

"Well, you've seen the pictures..."

At the start of proceedings on the second day, the lawyers were called to a meeting with the judge in his chambers. The courtroom remained quiet, as if they might overhear what was being said, but after a while people began to talk, to chatter, until Marsh's lawyer emerged alone. Silence fell. He leaned over his client and spoke briefly. Marsh shook his head. The lawyer returned to the judge's chambers and shortly after they all came out again. This time it was the turn of Mary's lawyer to shake his head. Up on the bench, the judge's gavel came down.

"Due to last minute evidence," he said, "I'm throwing this case out of court. I understand that the defendant finds his marriage now to be untenable and wishes to start his own divorce proceedings right away."

The Press never printed the reason for the collapse of the case, and Billy made up stories about how the judge had been bribed by the Castor Oil King. But Longman believed what the Mary Marsh's lawyers told them afterwards was true. Late in the day, the defence council had presented the judge with affidavits from two independent gynaecologists. Miss Dare was a virgin. They had not intended to use this evidence but they were concerned that the case was not going their way.

Mary Marsh's alimony was not as much as she wanted, but there was little she could do. Those close to her had long suspected she had set the whole thing up to get her hands on the fortune belonging to a man she no longer cared for. Although she lost the case, it did the detective no harm. Longman's name was in the papers, business prospered, and Ruth Mason let him off a month's rent while he was waiting for Mrs Marsh to settle her bill.

Dick Longman married Flora Pidgin and they had two daughters. Edie was the first and on her fifth birthday Longman had raced down to Schwarz to try to find her some gifts. He could not fail to notice a poster in the book department advertising a new bestseller from Doubleday. It was called *The Lonely Doll* and it was by "*this year's most promising new author, Dare Wright*".

Longman picked up a copy. It had around fifty pages, with photographs on each page. The pictures were familiar. Though there was little in the background, he was sure that they had been taken in Room 512 at the Bristol Hotel. Certainly the doll looked like the one he had incidentally snapped. The story was about a teddy bear who came to stay and how he led her astray, and how the bear's father put her across his knee and spanked her for misbehaving. There were photographs on every page.

"Can I help you, sir?" an assistant asked.

"I was just looking for a gift for my five-year-old." Longman put the book down. "But she doesn't like to read so much. I think I'll try the games department."

17: VOLTAIRE AND THE DOGS OF ST BERNARD

**Hôtel Bristol
Geneva, Switzerland
www.bristol.ch**

It was Barry who finally came between me and Sophie. I did not have a chance. For some time my long-standing partner had been pining for a dog, saying that she wanted some company when I wasn't around, which, it is true, was much of the time. She even went so far as to accuse me of preferring hotels to my own home, an accusation I denied, though on reflection, given the service, the convenience and lack of responsibility, I wondered if she was not right. A less demanding animal, a goldfish, a hamster or even a cat was out of the question. So was a child. We were both wrapped up in our careers and didn't feel ready for parenthood. But a dog, apparently, was a different matter. The idea of people in cities owning dogs has always been anathema to me, and our Docklands apartment was quite unsuitable for raising even the meanest of curs.

"Does a horse need a dog?" I asked one rare Sunday morning that found us so comfortably settled in bed with our laptops and papers that she had thought it safe to bring up the pet question again. "Or a sheep need koi carp? No other animal depends on another. Humans enslave animals simply for their own gratification. Dogs are born free, yet everywhere they are on leads."

She kicked off the duvet and jumped on top of me. "There is no beast happier than a dog with a good master." Her long tongue started slapping against my cheek. "And it would be nice to live with a beast that does not argue all the time."

I rolled up a newspaper, smacked her nose with it and told her to get back in her kennel.

Our disagreements were not always so playful, and as my

absences became longer, they became sharper. Then one night on the phone from Geneva, her mother told her that the St Bernard dogs in the Great Bernardine Hospice were being sold off for 1,700 Swiss francs a pup, and the next thing I knew she was on a plane to Switzerland. I feared the worst.

St Bernard dogs had been at the alpine monastery-hospice since around the mid-17th century. These great ugly slavering brutes were bred here because their broad chests could plough through deep snowdrifts, their acute sense warned of impending avalanches, and they had the ability to sniff out life, or even a corpse. Their hospice home is in the Alps' oldest pass, which connects the Aosta Valley in Italy with the Valois in Switzerland. This was the high point of the Via Delle Gallie, paved by the Romans and used as their route to France and Britain, and the first dogs to arrive in the region probably came with them.

The pass climbs to 2,472 metres and is open only from June to September. Winter snowdrifts can reach forty feet and avalanches are not infrequent. It was a perilous crossing for the early trickle of tradesmen, artisans, labourers, beggars, messengers, ambassadors and *romeros*, Christian pilgrims on their way to the tomb of St Peter in Rome. Some travellers were so terrified of the precipitous paths that they insisted on being blindfolded by their guides and led by the hand. The violence of man in the shape of robbers and thugs added to the unkindness of nature, while the threat of wolves and bears, let alone the witches, demons and dragons known to inhabit the summits, amounted to a powerful disincentive to venture within a hundred miles of the mountains. In fact the Alps were so feared that most travellers from northern Europe en route to Rome would rather the much longer sea voyage, via Finisterre, Biscay and Gibraltar. But not everyone had the time or money to go that way, while some pilgrims believed, or were led to believe, that this gamble with death was part of the price of their penitence.

Concerned at the number of victims of both man and the elements on the mountain passes, the archdeacon of Aosta decided to act. Bernard of Menthon, whose family castle was near Annecy, had abandoned his bride on the eve of his high-society wedding to join the Augustine order and preach to the unconverted of the Alps. (What happened to his humiliated bride is not recorded, though she was probably forced into a nunnery by his betrayal.) Archdeacon Bernard took it on himself to build, at his own expense, a monastery at the pass, which today marks the Swiss-Italian border. This was consecrated in AD 962. Bernard thus ensured himself a place as patron saint of mountaineers and skiers. It also ensured that his name would be ever associated with a dog.

Prior Ballalu was the first incumbent of the Great St Bernard monastery to mention dogs, in 1708. He also wrote about a wheel that had been invented by Canon Vincent Camos in which a dog was employed to turn the kitchen spit. The kitchen must have been a warm and generous place compared to the bleak, unheated cells and solid beds offered to guests. They were allowed to stay no more than three nights, their food and drink had to be paid for and donations were always sought.

The hospice was well stocked. When Napoleon's Armée d'Italie came through here in 1800 his 35,000 troops each received bread and cheese and a glass of wine, for which they were charged 18,960 francs 95 centimes. Napoleon asked Prior Murith for his copy of Livy so he could look up the account of Hannibal crossing the Alps with his elephants, to see if this might be the same pass. No answer to this question has ever satisfactorily been given.

Thirty years before Napoleon made the crossing, the 4th Earl of Bristol made his first visit to the monastery on his way to Rome. The Canons Regular of St Augustine were all at dinner when he arrived, and the porter would not let him in. When Bristol protested that he was a bishop, the porter conveyed the news to the Prior, who came scurrying at once, with all due apology, having received no forewarning of this honoured visit. All the monks then knelt before Bristol who made a great show of offering his benediction, after which he joined them in the refectory for a meal. By the time of his second visit the Prior and the fraternity had realised that they had been tricked by a Protestant bishop, and his reception was far from warm. In the visitors book Bristol wrote:

"If second thoughts are best, second visits are not always so... I quit the place (to use a fashionable expression) more penetrated with cold than the civility of the house; more loaded with compliments than with food; and after seeing two swaggering Capuchins pass through the portico with their paunches as full as their wallets, I cannot help remembering the Scripture expression: he hath filled the hungry with good things, but the rich He hath sent empty away."

There was something about Catholic countries that brought out a childish exhibitionism in Bristol. Once, in Siena, he was sitting down to dinner when the Corpus Christi procession carrying the Host passed beneath his window. Irritated by the sound of their endless bells, Bristol opened the window and poured a tureen of pasta on the procession. In the ensuing rumpus, he and his valet were forced to make a swift getaway out of the back of the building, bribing anyone who came near and hiding until night fell and they found horses to whisk them clear of the Duchy of Tuscany.

He further enraged the Catholic authorities when he attended the annual Maunday Thursday washing of feet by the Pope in the Sistine Chapel in Rome. This act represented Christ's humility, and His Holiness was not meant to display his earthly pomp, but that was no reason for Bristol to arrive not in the severe black of his daily office, but in full Anglican regalia, in his white linen rochet over which his red silk chimere dazzled, as if he himself were about to offer the sacraments. *"The Bishop of Derry most absurdly appeared in his English bishop's dress,"* wrote Sir Edward Newenham, an Irish politician who was also attending the ceremony in the Sistine Chapel that day. *"He was laughed at by everyone. For this piece of absurdity he was obliged to go to the lowest part of the chapel among the common people while my sons and I were in the same upper division with the Cardinals. After this behaviour the eccentric bishop was held in the greatest contempt. Scarcely a nobleman would visit him."*

It is hard to imagine the Bishop gave a fig; each fresh outrage was just another tale to add to his cache of anecdotes that were always on hand to impress new acquaintances, or to amuse such old flames as Emma Hamilton and the Countess of Lichtenau.

By the spring of 1803, a few months before his death at the age of seventy-two, Lord Bristol had become a public spectacle in Rome. Catherine Wilmot, a young Irish woman travelling with Lord and Lady Mount Cashell, thought him *"one of the greatest curiosities alive"* and described him as both profane and a reprobate. After seeing him from the window of her hotel, she wrote, *"His figure is little, and his face very sharp and wicked; on his head he wore a purple velvet nightcap with a tassel of gold hanging over his shoulders and a sort of mitre in the front; silk stockings and slippers of the same colour, and a short round petticoat such as Bishops wear, fringed with gold about the knee. A loose dressing gown of silk was then thrown over his shoulders. In this Merry Andrew trim he rode on horse back to the never ending amusement of all the beholders! The last time I saw him he was sitting in his carriage between two Italian women, dress'd in white Bed-gown and Night-cap like a witch and giving himself the airs of an Adonis."*

It was hardly surprising that Bristol's devotion to his office and to his maker were frequently called into question. In a letter from Paris on the eve of the French Revolution, he had written to his daughter Louise, *"…I do not yet believe in the States General, the Resurrection of the dead, the forgiveness of Sins, nor Patriotism everlasting."* Some concluded that he was simply a deist, like Voltaire, whom he greatly admired, and believed that religions are different because they are devised by man, but morality is the same everywhere because it is devised by God. Perhaps that was why Bristol was so supportive of Catholic emancipation in Ireland. It was Voltaire who had declared that if God did not exist it would be necessary to invent him, though he also believed, in his enlightened age, that "One hundred years from my day there will not be a Bible in the earth except one that is looked upon by an antiquarian curiosity seeker".

On that first journey through the St Bernard Pass to Rome, Lord Bristol was on a personally conceived mission to try to find some acceptable form of wording for an oath of allegiance that Irish Catholics might take so that they could stand for parliament without offending either the pope or the British monarchy. Immediately prior to his stay at the monastery, he had visited Voltaire, who had been thrown out of Geneva for illegally staging plays and was living at the nearby seigneurial estate at Fernay, which he had recently purchased. Bristol's mission intrigued the French playwright and philosopher, who was by now devoting his life to campaigning against the use of institutional torture, and as they made their adieus, he asked Bristol to bring back from Rome the ears of the Inquisitor General. Bristol duly delivered the request to Clement XIV who was apparently amused by the idea, but no breakthrough was made in either the powers of the Inquisition, or in the emancipation of Catholics in Britain.

As a young man exiled in London, Voltaire had known Bristol's parents. John, Lord Hervey of Ickworth, who missed out on the Bristol title, was a bisexual dandy, a highly successful Vice-Chamberlain of the Household and later Lord Privy Seal at the court of George II where he was Queen Caroline's closest confidant. It was to John Hervey that Lady Montague was referring when she said, "There are men, women and Herveys." This was as much on account of John Hervey's eccentricity as his bisexuality, which Alexander Pope referred to less obliquely:

> *Amphibious thing! That acting either part,*
> *The trifling head or the corrupted heart!*
> *Fop at the toilet, flatterer at the board,*
> *Now trips a lady, and now struts a lord.*

Lord Hervey was undoubtedly charismatic and a master of court intrigue, and when his shockingly revelatory *Memoirs from the Court of George II* was first published a century after his death, it still had to be censored. Despite his foppish homosexuality, he had married out of love and fathered eight children. Frederick Augustus, their third son, who was to become our Earl-Bishop, was named after the Prince of Wales, heir to the throne, who was his godfather.

Frederick's mother, Mary "Molly" Lepel, Lady Hervey, was no less a social high flyer. Intelligent, charming and attractive, she was a lady-in-waiting to the Princess of Wales. Alexander Pope wrote glowingly of her and so did Voltaire, whose bold declaration of love is his only known poem in English (despite the invocation of "Hervey", it is Molly, not John, to whom this verse is dedicated):

> *Hervey, would you know the passion*
> *You have kindled in my breast*
> *Trifling is the inclination*
> *That by words can be express'd*
>
> *In my silence see the lover;*
> *True love is silence known;*
> *In my eyes you'll best discover*
> *All the powers you own.*

John Hervey, too, wrote poetry, and he also travelled on the Continent. Returning from an official trip to Florence with his lover Stephen Fox, the Earl of Ilchester, in 1729, he sent a lengthy description of the journey to his wife Molly. Its contents is of rather greater interest than its style.

> *Pursuant then to my design,*
> *From Florence, fam'd for silk and wine,*
> *To Pisa first we bend our course,*
> *And vile the inn, tho' I've found worse.*
> *Our beds were musty, course our fare,*
> *And gnats extremely busy there...*

To Lerici we take our road:
But there we made no long abode;
We supp'd and then to bed we went,
Not for rest, but punishment.
For fleas and bugs kept such a rout
That Pisa's gnats were nothing to't...

To tell you how the Alps we pass'd
A dreadful journey. I remember,
Twas hardly worse ev'n last November
Imagine, child! our piteous plight,
No food by day, no rest by night.
How wet, how comfortless, how cold,
We passe'd Mount Sinis, can't be told.
Impervious to a chaise, we rode
In chairs, eight human creatures load,
Twelve miles beneath our weight they groan
Five up, five plain away, two down.

Mount Senis is today called Mount Cenis and the "chair" that John Hervey describes would have been a *caris*, a kind of sled with a rush bottom that had been devised to take travellers across the pass. One porter pulled at the front, another steered from behind, and if the vehicle got out of control they would jump clear and leave the occupants to do the same. If the twelve bumpy miles Hervey describes were uncomfortable for the English lords, they must have been even more gruelling for the porters. At that time no wheeled vehicle had ever penetrated the Alps. It was not until 1775, five years after Hervey's son had preyed on the hospitality of Great St Bernard, that the first carriage made it from Italy into France, when Sir William Hamilton's nephew Charles Greville went to the immense expense of having his carriage pulled across the St Gotthard Pass.

Hervey's complaint about the inns of Italy was to be echoed by his contemporaries in most parts of Europe throughout the

18th century. Inns in Switzerland, however, were on the whole better than most, not least because local laws began to stipulate what a meal should consist of, and how much it should cost, though English travellers, who made up the greatest numbers of visitors, frequently wrote of the high price of lodging. Rooms in a community's larger houses, perhaps belonging to the local pastor or mayor, were rented out, and accommodation was added as demand increased.

It has been suggested that the tradition of good hotel-keeping in Switzerland has its origin in the peace congress held for six months in Baden in 1714 at the end of hostilities between France and the Holy Roman Empire in the War of the Spanish Succession. From May to September, when the treaty was finally signed, every room in the Swiss spa town was taken. Among the international delegates and long-staying guests were forty-two sovereign princes. They were a demanding crowd, and gave many lessons in exactly what European nobility expected for their daily comforts and how they should be served. The inn keepers would not have been surprised to discover that the aristocracy could and did do exactly as they pleased, but when the French ambassador decided that his rooms were too small and simply had the walls torn down, it was also a lesson in how letting a guest do as he wants also allows the manager to charge what he likes. There was money to be made here.

Tourism, the largest global industry of the 21st century, began in Switzerland. For the first time people discovered how to travel not for education or pilgrimage, but purely for pleasure, and their numbers increased steadily throughout the 18th and 19th centuries. Thomas Cook organised the world's first package holiday here in 1863, and Americans apparently came because it was the one place in Europe where they could guarantee that cream would be served with their coffee. The season was short, lasting barely two months, in the late 19th and early 20th centuries when winter holidays began. If there was any local resentment about this influx of tourists, it was tempered by the fact that, being a mountainous country, Switzerland had been unable to support its own population. Village economies had come to rely on remittance money, much of it from young men hired around Europe as mercenaries in Swiss regiments and as palace guards.

The development of the hotel industry in this land-locked country led to the world's first hotel management school opening in Lausanne in 1893. Switzerland soon became the recognised hotel centre of the world, to which students from all corners of the globe flocked to learn the art of good service. As for Swiss Bristols, they were liberally scattered and can still be found in Adelboden, Berne, Davos, Geneva, Lukerbad, Lugano, Montreux, Sass-Fee, Verbier, Villars, Zermatt and Zurich.

The Hôtel Bristol in Geneva was my next stop. Built in 1898 in Rue du Mont Blanc, a stone's throw from the Pont du Mont Blanc, which crosses the western corner of Lake Geneva, the hotel is one of the city's finest, with four stars and a hundred rooms. I booked in a few weeks after Sophie had disappeared. She had left in pursuit of a St Bernard without further word and had not been in touch since. Her possessions had vanished with her. More disastrously, my invaluable postcard collection was missing; she had disappeared on the day the dustmen came. It was a terrible double blow. The only glimmer of light was that our flat was rented, so there was no problem with dividing up any capital. Otherwise nothing was owing; Sophie had left no trace.

After more than a week, her office told me that she had returned to their Geneva branch, and I imagined she would have retreated to her parents' home, or at least they would know where she was. Because her family's lakeside villa is only a few kilometres from Geneva and they had always been hospitable, I had never had reason to stay in a hotel in the city before. They were not a particularly warm couple, and in spite of my speculation about Patrice's infidelity causing Fernande to make her trip to the Czech Republic, they remained together. Patrice was a lawyer, and he usually had a few good stories and gossip, some of it gleaned through the telescope that he kept trained on the lake from his attic *garçonnière*. There was one well-known actor's house and garden on the opposite side of the lake that he took particular interest in chronicling.

But I wasn't here for any idle chat. Neither of them was speaking to me now. Conversations with them had become abrupt and Fernande, when I managed to speak to her, refused to say anything about Sophie's whereabouts. The break-up of our relationship was clearly being seen as entirely my fault, just as Fernande's failure to secure a stake in the Carlsbad Bristol Hotel, now a magnificent and thriving spa, had undoubtedly been blamed on me.

Finally, after three weeks, I managed to catch Sophie at her office in Geneva, but all she would say was that it was all over between us and there was no point in speaking any more.

"Is there somebody else?" I asked.

"Only Barry."

"Barry?"

"The dog."

The conversation lasted less than a minute. I didn't even have the opportunity to ask her what she had done with my Hotel Bristol postcards. Hurled into that madness of the rejected lover who is persuaded, against all reason, that if only we could just sit down and talk, then everything might be resolved, I lost the ability to concentrate. Work was being left undone. Streets were paced over and over again. My temper was increasingly short. On the phone to her parents once more I heard a dog bark in the echoing hall and I sailed rudderless into the uncharted waters of despair. It was like a death without a proper funeral. Something had to be done.

An early Saturday flight from the London City airport meant that I reached Geneva and the Hôtel Bristol before noon. From my deluxe double room overlooking the lake, which I had booked on the slimmest chance I could persuade her back, I dialled the villa from the bedside phone. Rita, the Romanian maid, answered. "*Elle n'est pas là.*" Usually she spoke to me in English; French was a new barrier. When I tried to ascertain what time Sophie might return to the house, she said "*Sais pas*" in such an insolent way that I cursed all Romanians and wished for the immediate collapse of their economy. Just before she put down the phone I heard the villa's distant doorbell ring, by which I mean the gate bell, because there was a long drive and an electric iron gate with an intercom that separated the house from the outside world. It set the dog barking. Barry was laughing at me, I could tell.

Enraged, I hired a car and drove up to the Great St Bernard Pass. It was a grey day in early spring, with slush by the road and traffic everywhere, the lorries climbing with deliberate slowness just to annoy me. There was nothing romantic about the mountain pass now, no drama in the snowy summits that were half buried in cloud, nothing faintly interesting in the solid monastic buildings, nothing to connect me with the stories of the Earl-Bishop in which I had once been so immersed. I entered the Hospice and rang the reception bell. When a young monk appeared I demanded to know about the dogs for sale.

"They are very popular." He was sublimely courteous and spoke far too slowly. "Of course, we use German Shepherds now, but we still breed St Bernard's, so the tradition is not entirely dead. You know the story of the St Bernard's? The brandy barrels, they are just an invention... "

I was hardly listening to him. I had had enough of history, of anecdotes and tired old tales. Only the future concerned me now. He took me through to the kennels. One pup was left from the last litter. It was a runtish whelp, a curled up red-and-white lump of stupidity. God knows why or what I thought I was going to do with it, but I bought the puppy then and there. After I had purchased a basket, blankets, collar, lead and a few days' supply of dog food, the bill drifted over 2,000 Swiss Francs. *Tant pis.*

I sped back down to the lake, with the dog whimpering in the back of the car. It was getting dark by this time. I headed through Geneva and along the north side of the lake towards the villa. There was a car park by a landing stage where row boats were for rent. No one was around. Chucking the dog in the back of one of the boats I cast off. The wind was getting up, and spray came over the bow. Let it blow, let it rain. The dog whimpered and kept low; a startled look never left him. "Where's the bloody brandy barrel now?" I shouted at him. Trembling, he wriggled as far from me as he could. It was twenty minutes before I was opposite the villa where I was glad to see there were a few lights on, particularly in the small attic window. I took out my mobile and dialled the house. Sophie's mother answered.

"I am out on the lake," I yelled against the wind. "Tell Patrice to look through the telescope from the attic and he will see me in the row boat with Barry's little brother." I took the puppy by the scruff of its neck, stood up unsteadily in the choppy water, and held it triumphantly in the air. "I want to see Sophie, Fernande, and I want to see her now. If she doesn't call me within fifteen minutes and arrange a meeting, the puppy goes overboard."

It worked. Half an hour later Sophie and I were sitting in the car outside the villa by the lake. It was dark and the heavy rain had drenched us all, most notably the puppy, who sat like a pile of wet laundry in her lap soaking her Burberry. Her scarf and shoes, in matching maroon, were new. The engine was running to keep the car heater roaring, and the windows became misty white. Passing cars lit the interior intermittently.

"Mamma didn't believe you would drown him, but I told her you would." She stared at her hand as it moved kindly down the length of the dog's back.

"I was desperate to see you."

"You have become cold and heartless."

I did not try to defend myself. Other truths were at work. Perhaps she had uncovered a small peccadillo of mine, a misdemeanour I had neglected to mention, an infelicity, an insensitivity, an infidelity. But she asked nothing of me. She did not want me at all. The only thing she would say was that she really needed a change.

"That's no reason to avoid me," I said. "We're adults. We should be able to talk this through."

"No. This is the only way I can make a proper break." Her voice was growing firmer. "If I talk to you, it would only confuse everything, and I have been confused too much already, for a long time. But now my mind is made up. It isn't easy for me either, you know."

So I was meant to feel sorry for her. I didn't apologise, but in the end I had to admit defeat. I had done all I could, nearly sacrificing the life of an innocent dog in the process. What man could have done more? Staring through the windscreen into the dripping darkness, I contemplated the future without Sophie and wondered, aloud, what on earth I was going to do with the St Bernard. I had no idea if they permitted dogs at the Hôtel Bristol.

"I'll look after him." Sophie bent and kissed the puppy's ear. A heavy sigh made his whole body tremble.

I felt a last pang of jealousy. "Will you keep him?"

"I'll take him back to the monastery in the morning."

This was a double rejection. First me, now my dog.

She tickled him behind the ear. I could barely watch. "Does he have a name?"

"Voltaire."

She kissed his ear again. He was her new love. Lucky dog. He knew no reason and could therefore do no wrong. "I don't think I ever met a dog called Voltaire before."

She was talking to him, not to me. She was chatting him up. I was barely there.

But at least we had finally managed to have something resembling a conversation. The encounter had calmed me down. For a moment I thought she might turn her face towards me, that I would see some regret in her eyes, a realisation that a wrong decision had been made, and we would kiss. But in my heart I knew that I had handed my baton on, to Barry and to Voltaire.

She took the puppy in her arms, and I got out of the car to help her. The gates opened through some divine intervention and I watched as she walked away from me up the drive towards the villa. She did not look back.

On the slow, traffic-lined road back to Geneva, I turned on the radio and listened to Debussy's *La Mer*, watching the city lights swim in the abysmally dark waters of the lake. Soon a hot shower would revive me, and the only challenge of the evening would be deciding what to choose from the restaurant menu. And what nightcap would be most suitable in the piano bar.

In the comfort of a Bristol once more, where the service was as faultless as one might expect from a top-class Swiss hotel, and the parameters of life were constrained by recognisable rhythms and rules, I would be safe from any further emotional harm.

18: Jazz on a Cold Winter's Night

**Hotel Bristol
Oslo, Norway
wwwbristol.no**

A retired manager of the Dunlop tyre and rubber company once told me that during a lifetime of working abroad, he had been well looked after by his employers.

"I always travelled First Class," he said, "and I never boarded an aeroplane without meeting at least one other passenger I knew. Aeroplanes for us were like a club. You'd chat and have drinks and soon get to know a few more people. It was all very sociable."

I travel Club or Business Class wherever I go and I am always amazed at the number of people in the world that I do not know. If there is a familiar face on board, it usually belongs to somebody who has appeared either on television or in the papers where they created such a fleeting impression that I can't put a name to them. Sometimes I have a fantasy about two people meeting and having an affair, neither of whom has the slightest idea that the other is phenomenally famous in their particular field of endeavour. Only when they start dating publicly and are mobbed by their separate fans, do they realise what a star the other one is to a whole section of the population.

There was nobody I knew in Club Class on the flight to Oslo at the beginning of December 2005, but among the passengers there were certain to be several politicians and celebrities heading for the Norwegian capital for the annual three-day Nobel Peace Prize jamboree. That year's winner, Dr Mohammed ElBaradei, director of the International Atomic Energy Agency, may well have been among them. I had no idea what the Egyptian scientist looked like, even though I had requested a meeting with him to discuss the best way to handle the windfall, which he was donating to his sister's Cairo orphanage. I have had some luck with long shots in the past and always believe they are worth a try. We had one or two business acquaintances in common, so it wasn't entirely a cold call, but I had not yet received a reply.

Club Class passengers tend either to travel in bunches or alone. I was seated next to a young woman of university age who for all I knew was an aspiring world figure, or the daughter of one; perhaps her daddy had bought her ticket. She had a fresh, open, confident face and waves of dark hair that curled around her shoulders. She looked a little like Sophie. Since we had separated, an increasing number of women did.

Hers was the window seat, mine the aisle, and we briefly said hello as I settled in beside her. The wire from an iPod earphone led beneath her hair and when we began to taxi down the runway, she opened a paperback, cracking its spine. Perhaps she was trying to divert her mind from the take-off. The book was entitled *Lust*. As the plane gathered speed and rose through the grey London clouds she took out a pencil and began underlining words and phrases with deliberate care. By the time we reached 30,000 feet I had decided that either Erotic Studies must be on her university syllabus or she was rehearsing for a role in a Scandinavian orgy, and it made me all too aware of the current lack of excitement in my own life. *The Financial Times* remained in my briefcase and I flipped though the pages of the glossy in-flight magazine. It included a brief guide to Oslo, a city I did not know well, and I was gratified to see a recommendation for the Bristol Lounge at the Bristol Hotel, where there was live music every evening after 10pm. Of course I was booked into the Bristol. There was also an article on the continuing search for Edvard Munch's *The Scream*, which had been snatched along with *The Madonna* in a daring raid from the city's Munch Museum in the August of the previous year. Both paintings were illustrated in the magazine, and I realised that I had been wrong about the young woman sitting next to me. It wasn't Sophie she looked like, it was Munch's

Madonna. In fact the similarity was so striking that I felt a sudden rush of embarrassment and quickly turned the page so she wouldn't catch me looking at her naked torso.

At the first clatter of the lunch trolley, I stood up to allow my neighbour out to visit the loo. *Lust* was left on her seat and I took the opportunity to discover exactly what it was she was reading. The book was written by Elfriede Jelinek, winner of the Nobel Prize for Literature the previous year and author of *The Piano Player*, which had been made into a film. The words "voyeur'" and "sadism" came to mind. I flipped through the text. Words and phrases that the student had been underlining were forceful and in some cases cruel, violent and crude. "*He roasts his hefty sausage in her oven, in its flaky pastry case of hair and skin...* "

On her return I looked at her quite differently, not as an ingenu student, but as a hard nosed little sadist. She seemed so young and tender, it was difficult to imagine. I watched her fingers as they began exploring the contenst of her meal tray. They were long and slim, the nails thick and uneven; one was broken. I needed to know more. After exchanging a few empty remarks about aeroplane food, I nodded towards the book that she had just put away.

"Jelinek's rather dark, don't you think?" I ventured.

She leaned her head back and her tawny eyes narrowed as she turned to address me. "If you take sexual violence against women as the starting point and template not just for Western culture but for culture in every part of the world, I can't see there's much room for sunshine." Her voice was soft and lyrical, with an accent I could not quite put my finger on.

"Is that your starting point, too?"

She tore open a pepper sachet with her teeth. "Ask any psychiatrist in any country around the world what constitutes the biggest number of his or her cases and they will tell you that it's the abuse of women." She did not sound angry at this state of affairs; she was merely passing on what she knew. "It has nothing to do with race or religion. It goes on in South Africa, in India,

Australia, in all the Americas. In Britain one in four women in a relationship suffer physical abuse. And it's not just among the poor and ignorant. In the United States, in middle-class New England, it's endemic. And look at Guatemala now, nearly a decade after the Oslo Peace Accord ended thirty years of civil war in which the most disgusting acts were perpetrated against women... have you read Rigoberta Menchú's book?"

I nodded. I hadn't, but I knew that *I, Rigoberta Menchú* had brought the human rights campaigner the Nobel Peace Prize in 1992. It was around that time that my brother James had begun working among the Mayans in Central America and he had been enthusiastic about the Guatamalan's award and what it would mean to the local people. Flaking off small forkfuls of salmon from her main course, the student went on to tell me in detail, which I could have done without, about how young girls in Guatemala City today were being raped and killed without their cases being pursued. No arrests were ever made. A culture had built up, but it was not surprising. It was only an excess of what was going on everywhere.

Staring out of aeroplane windows, looking down on the silent, unfolding earth, it was impossible not to adopt a god's eye view of the chaos and savagery that lay so completely hidden below. And on a flight headed for Oslo, a city that has become synonymous with peace, with its brave optimism of "Initiatives" "Agreements", "Tunnels" and "Accords", everyone on board must have spent some time during the three-hour flight ruminating on the state of the world.

When the trays were cleared away our conversation concluded and the student picked up her book and plugged in her iPod. We didn't speak again until the plane had taxied to a halt and I had fetched our thick coats and luggage down from the overhead locker. Her bag was small; there was a much larger one, she said, in the hold. While we waited in silence for the mobile corridor to be anchored to the exit door, I asked her if she was catching any of the weekend's big events.

"I'll be at the concert on Sunday."

"Me, too. We're lucky to get tickets. They sold out fast."

"Are you with one of the peace organisations?"

"No, most of my clients are entirely selfish. My job is to make people rich. And you?"

"I sing for my supper."

She made it sound casual, an off-hand remark, but I suddenly realised who she was. Not her name, but her presence. She didn't need a ticket for the concert. She didn't need her daddy to buy her a Club Class ticket. She was a singer, someone that people like me had paid to see. I had completely misjudged her, assuming, because of her age, that she was still in education. Now I realised I was standing next to an international performer, perhaps even, to some, a star. But her face was not familiar and all I could do was ask rather lamely, "Are you famous?"

She smiled. Her teeth were all straight and very white. "My Mum thinks I am."

Not wanting to ask her name in case it meant even less to me than her face, and convinced that a number of people in Club Class were now eavesdropping, knowing exactly who she was and how ignorant I was, it was a relief when the door finally opened and we went on our way. In the passport queue we lost contact and with only hand luggage, I was soon ahead of most of the passengers. Ignoring dismissive looks from the knots of autograph hunters in the Arrivals Lounge, I was soon outside in the afternoon darkness where a taxi whisked me away towards the ice-packed pavements glinting beneath the street lights.

The city is not one of the world's most beautiful but, set by the water's edge with narrow streets and low-level traffic, it has a friendly, intimate air. And with snow on the ground, skaters in the central park and candlelight flickering from every window, it embraced winter warmly. Christmas was not far off, and though I would do my shopping in Paris and fly down to my parents in the heat of Southern Spain on Christmas Day, Oslo was a far more seasonal place to be.

The Oslo Bristol, sister of the Hotel Bristol Stephanie in Brussels, is in the centre of town, in Kristian IV's Gate. Built in 1920 in northern neo-Gothic style, with a new wing added in 2000 to give it 250 rooms, this is a fine old establishment, a tranquil spot in a calm town. It lies a block from the parliament and the new Nobel Peace Center, a couple of blocks from the waterfront and a spit away from the city's slightly more prestigious Grand Hotel where ElBaradei would be staying in the Nobel Suite. His rooms offered a choice of two balconies from where he could wave to the welcoming crowds. At dinner in the hotel's Mirror Room that evening he would be the guest of King Harald and the Nobel Committee.

I was locked in various meetings while ElBaradei was giving his speech in the City Hall the following morning, but at the end of the day, after a sauna, I replayed the event in my hotel room. Tall, dignified, moustachioed and well spoken, he was easily recognisable. His plea for the rich to do more for the poor was as old as time, but it was impressive and it made me want to meet him even more. I left a phone message for him at the desk of the Grand Hotel, knowing that I would not be the only person wishing for an audience.

The sun refused to make an appearance on Sunday. I spent thirty minutes in the gym before a morning engagement and lunchtime drinks with some embassy people. A 3.30 meeting with a Dutch charity fund manager at the Grand Hotel was due to conclude my business in Oslo, leaving me free to enjoy the concert in the Oslo Spektrum Arena. I was particularly looking forward to the finale of the whole jamboree when I would finally learn the identity of the singer whom I could now safely boast I once met. ("*We had lunch together recently. She had the salmon, I had the reindeer, and we had a long discussion about Rigoberto Manchú and the Mayans. Terribly interesting. Surely you've read Rigoberto Manchú...?*)

Wrapped in a heavy wool coat and scarf, leather gloves and thermal hat, I had just stepped from the Bristol into the afternoon darkness to walk the short distance to my meeting at the Grand when a black Volvo drew up to the kerb in front of me. A young man in shiny dark blue padded jacket and thermal beanie, from which strands of blond hair escaped, stepped out of the passenger door and turned towards me.

"Mr Cotton, Dr ElBaradei can see you now, if you would like to come with us." His English was near perfect and his words drifted up to the street light in great misty clouds. "He is not in his hotel at the moment; he is visiting a minister in a cottage a few miles from the city. This is the only opportunity he will have of meeting you here. He does not have much time because of course he has to be at this evening's concert."

"Of course," I climbed into the back of the car barely able to hide my delight.

As we sped away, I took out my phone and rescheduled the Dutchman. He was a little put out, but at the mention of the Nobel Laureate he could not complain, and my reputation could only go up. The journey from the city was just one long dark tunnel framed with snowy pine fronds and I had no idea where we were going, nor really cared. My speech to the Egyptian scientist did not need rehearsing; I had used it to try to extract money from beneficiaries a dozen times before. So I settled down to the amiable conversation of the driver and his companion who talked about Oslo, jazz and the Hotel Bristol. In English delivered with more enthusiasm than fluency, the driver said that his grandfather had played trumpet for the Hotel Bristol Orchestra, which had become the Norwegian Radio Orchestra.

"Bristol is famous for music," he said. "Most famous. Five Jazzing Devils came here in 'twenty-one. The year Bristol opens. First American jazz band visit Norway. Very very first." He wanted to know if I had heard any live music since I had arrived. When I said that I hadn't, he recommended a place which he said had "real cool music, real cool".

In a while we drew off the main road and for fifteen minutes we trundled down bumpy, icy lanes before the dim orange glow of a curtained room defined a log cabin. The man who greeted us at the door was middle-aged, bald and about my height. The traditional, brightly patterned Norwegian sweater he wore exaggerated his bulk, making him seem more powerfully built than probably was the case.

"You may wish to keep your coat on, Mr Cotton," he said. "I am afraid there is no central heating in the cottage."

The temperature inside was not much above the tumbling temperature outside, and I kept my hat and gloves on, too, as he ushered me into a sparsely furnished sitting room. There was a long dining table and two dust-covered high-backed armchairs that faced into the room, each side of a glass-fronted stove, which glowed with aromatic pine logs. The walls and mantles were undecorated. There was no sign of the Nobel Laureate.

"Is Dr ElBaradei here?" I asked.

Nobody replied. The driver leaned back against the closed door. I took more notice of my hosts now. A scar near the driver's right eye made him look far less amiable than he had sounded from the back of the car. The young blond no longer possessed the confidence he had when he accosted me in the street. He had removed one of his gloves and his fingers were fidgeting, curling into heavy fists. With close-cropped grey hair and weather-worn features, the man in the Norwegian sweater looked as if he had spent much of his life on lonely cross-country skis, his pale eyes staring at endless snow, looking for trouble.

He went over to the armchair on the left and removed the dust sheet. It was not what it seemed. The chair's high back had been created by a painting placed on the seat. No explanation was necessary for what he was showing me. *The Scream* spoke – indeed it cried out – for itself. I glanced round the room. Why was I here? Why had they picked on me? This whole set up had nothing whatever to do with ElBaradei.

Taking a deep breath, I collected my thoughts and walked without hurrying over to the painting. It wasn't large, about two foot by three, but it was completely compelling. There was something both violent and pitiful about the distorted figure beside Oslo fjord, the blood-red sky, the blue-black water, and that unending wail passing through nature. The picture had lost its frame and the board had a couple of knocks on one side, which somehow added to the anguish.

"Well, well."

What else could I say? I stood back and looked at my three abductors in turn. They were impassive. Then the man in the Norwegian sweater took the dust cover off the other chair to reveal *The Madonna*. It was even more powerful than *The Scream*. The sweeping, haunting figure was a mix of lust and love, vanity and vulnerability, arrogance and submission, motherhood and the full power and mystery of naked flesh. It was in worse shape than *The Scream*. A whole chunk was lost from the top right corner and it was damaged down both sides. Paint had chipped from one of her cheeks. No attempt had been made to repair it. An abduction. A rape. A battered woman. I thought of the singer on the plane, of her tossed dark hair and similar sideways look, of her world of suffering women. I turned back to *The Scream*. The two images seemed inextricably related.

"Art isn't my speciality," I said.

"No, but money is," said the Norwegian sweater.

"Who sent you after me?"

"We have one or two friends in common."

It was hard to know whether to be flattered or alarmed by my spreading reputation. This was almost out of my league. But not quite. "How do I know they weren't painted yesterday?"

"Touch them if you like. No alarms will go off here."

I didn't want to touch the *The Madonna*. She had been violated enough. I walked back to *The Scream* and ran my fingers over the surface, feeling the despairing lines of the distorted face. It was dry as a bone. I was touching a fortune. According to the in-flight magazine article on the plane, their market value was US$10.4 million. But in sixteen months the thieves obviously had been unable to find a buyer. They must have been through every villain and corrupt art dealer in the land, and now they had got down to me.

"Bit of a problem, aren't they?"

"Don't think of them like that, Mr Cotton," the blond said. His other glove was off now and his fingers couldn't keep still. "They don't mean to be a problem. They're just a couple of orphans in need of a good home."

My hair tingled. I scratched the scalp beneath my hat and wondered who might want to buy them. Only a megalomaniac would splash out several million pounds on something that would have to remain hidden and could never be talked about, never mind that he would never see his money again. But in my business, megalomaniacs were not hard to find.

"How can you prove they're the originals?"

The sweater turned *The Scream* around and took me through various markings on the unpainted side of the board. He had a list of other pointers for both of the paintings. It was a well rehearsed line. Then the blond produced a photograph. It was a print film, he assured me, not a digital picture that could be doctored. It showed the pictures against a blank wall with Saturday's newspaper and a front page picture of the crowds at the airport greeting Dr ElBaradei.

"Take it with you to show they are still in circulation," he said.

I declined. I didn't want to be found with any incriminating evidence. Finally I got around to asking how much they expected from the paintings.

"A million dollars," the Norwegian sweater said.

I nodded. They would take half that, and I could probably sell them for five times as much. It was a buyers' market. I didn't know much about art, but I knew people who did. Jean-Philippe in our Paris office was the art expert, and I was flying to Paris in the morning. I told the thieves I would be in touch and we worked out a means of communication.

Eventually, as we were leaving the cabin, the blond came up close to me and I felt a blunt metal rod digging into my side. "We needn't tell you what could happen to you if you talk to the police, do we?"

I was so insulted at such a suggestion that I couldn't think of anything to say. My contemptuous look sufficed.

By the time I arrived back at the Bristol the Peace Concert had already begun. It would take me half an hour to reach the Arena, and I no longer felt like going. ElBaradei's half a million euro prize seemed paltry now. Besides, during the time it took me to get over to the Arena the Madonna from the aeroplane might have sung her song and I would have missed it. I switched the television on in the hotel bedroom and joined 450 million viewers around the world watching ElBaradei's opening speech. Then two actresses came on, the evening's hostesses, and it all went like clockwork. The show was dripping with worthiness.

With one eye on the television I also began surfing the internet, to find out what I could about Edvard Munch and the art market. Each time hands clapped I turned back to the television. It was nearly an hour before applause greeted my singer from the plane. She stepped into the intimacy of the spotlights to perform her songs and I sat on the bed to watch. Bare-wasted, in a short skirt, high boots and glittering top, she was familiar now, or at least her song was, from the radio. It was a sugary, innocent song that was far removed from the dark passages of *Lust*. She sung two more numbers, was applauded, and left. I turned down the sound and went back to the internet until all the stars reappeared in a finale.

Afterwards, I was restless. I had not eaten. My mind was racing in many directions. I left the Bristol and took a taxi to the jazz club that the Volvo driver had recommended. He was sitting in a booth with his boyfriend. We did not acknowledge each other. The music was cool, real cool, just as he had said it would be, and I ordered a long vodka at the bar, wondering about what I was doing, making people rich, wondering what the singer was doing, making people happy. And wondering how Edvard Munch might make quite a few people both rich and happy.

It was long after midnight when I left the jazz club and took a cab back to the Bristol. There was life in the hotel. Music drew me towards the Bristol Lounge where there was standing room only. At the far end of the room a young pianist was playing some lively jazz and beside him was the singer. She had changed out of her concert clothes into a pair of jeans and a rough shirt. Her songs had become coarser, too: bluesy, earthy. They sounded under-rehearsed. Perhaps the couple were improvising. In the hushed silence that greeted her next song, I began to catch some of the lyrics.

"He roasts his hefty sausage in her oven,
In its flaky pastry case of hair and skin…"

In spite of the words, the song was not delivered with any degree of sexiness or provocation. It was angry. The words lifted from Elfriede Jelinek's *Lust* were in complete contrast to the sweet hit song she had just sung for the world. She sang three more numbers in a similar vein. At the last ovation, the pianist kissed her and they went over to a group of friends. She didn't see me, and if I had the opportunity to speak to her again, I am not sure what I would have said.

Before taking a taxi to the airport the next morning I called in at the National Gallery, which was just a few doors away from the hotel. There was another version of *The Scream* here, in oils, and I stood and looked at it, as if it might offer some clue as to what the future of its companion might be. Already I had decided that the first thing I would do was track down a laser technician who could cut the board into small pieces that would be easily exportable. All I had to do now was think of a way of putting the pieces back together again.

In the gallery shop I bought postcards of both *The Scream* and *The Madonna*. I didn't know where the singer was staying, but at the Bristol Hotel desk I asked if she had checked out yet. It was a good guess. She hadn't. They gave me a hotel envelope and I went to sit in the lounge. My pen hovered for a while. I could envisage either of these images on the cover of her next CD. "A change of direction", the critics would say. And I could imagine the songs, with lyrics taken from works by Elfriede Jelinek, Rigoberta Menchú and even by the winner of this year's Nobel Prize for Literature, Harold Pinter.

In the end I turned over *The Madonna* and wrote on the back: "*Looking forward to the release of 'The Songs of the Laureates' by the most famous singer I ever met travelling on a plane to Oslo – A Club Class fan.*"

I put both of the cards in the envelope, wrote her name on the outside, sealed it and took it over to the desk. Then I checked out and flew to Paris.

It was time to get seriously rich.

19: SUHA ARAFAT
AND THE HOPE DIAMOND

Le Bristol
Paris, France
www.lebristol.com

Rue du Faubourg Saint-Honoré just before Christmas is the place to be if you are seriously rich. Paris's most elegant shopping street is lit up as if, well, as if it were Christmas and Sugar Daddy Santa is coming to town. Dior, Féraud, Versace, Laroche, Hermes, Gaultier, Lanvin, Saint-Laurent... all their windows dazzle with immense discretion and no a price tag is in sight. If you have to ask how much an item is, don't even bother to walk inside. There are plenty of window-shoppers and a few buyers, too, in old-fashioned furs and chic hats, in labelled scarves, long boots and kid gloves. Taxis prowl, chauffeurs cruise.

Sophie bought a Lanvin dress on our weekend away here, a second skin of eau de nil silk that cost a couple of thousand euros and looked more like a million when she tried it on. It was worth every cent. Heads turned. No restaurants, theatres or even parties were good enough to show her off, it seemed to me. But now she was probably dressing for someone else, and there was no point in thinking about it.

I had not been back to Le Bristol in Rue du Faubourg Saint-Honoré in the dozen intervening years, nor had I ever seen the street lit up like this. Any moment I expected nature's perfectly designed snowflakes to come floating out of the gloomy sky, courtesy of the street traders' association. At Le Bristol, showers of golden lights spilled down the handsome stone façade, spread across its Art Deco glass canopy and dripped over the two topiaried bay trees that stood outside its gold-trimmed door. The doorman would know the names of everyone arriving and leaving on any given day, and when I stepped on to the red carpet to enter the building, he made the slightest movement towards me.

"*Monsieur?*"

I mentioned the name of the resident American CEO I was meeting for English tea in the Marie Antoinette Salon, and he tipped his peaked cap and turned away. I was just another businessman, nobody important. I pushed against the revolving door. Nothing happened. Then it started turning in the opposite direction. Confused, I stood back until its occupants spilled out, temporarily blocking my path. There were four of them and I recognised Pierre Rizk, the Lebanese financier. Beside him was a woman of medium height and comfortable size in a thick black wool coat, her long blonde hair escaping a Hermes headscarf. Aged around forty, with a soft, Rubenseque face accentuated by thin ruby lips and pencilled eyebrows, she looked a little tired beneath the make-up. I stepped aside and her dark eyes fixed quizzically on mine, as if she wondered what I was doing standing in her way. I could not immediately put a name to her face, though I was sure we had met before, and to fill this moment of slight unease I wished her a merry Christmas.

Her laugh was little more than an intake of breath, a single, rather harsh note of surprise. Her colleagues raised their eyebrows, nodded, frowned and looked away. "*Joyeux Noël,*" the woman said over her shoulder, leaving an image of a smile from her painted lips dissolving in the air, like Alice's Cheshire Cat. Trying to remember who on earth she was, I pushed in through the revolving door, and it was only as I was about to exit into the lobby that the penny dropped. I had just wished Yassar Arafat's widow the Christian season's greetings. I continued my revolution until I re-emerged on the street, where I was just in time to see their limousine drive away. I waved a hand lamely towards the tinted windows.

"There's something I forgot to give her," I said to the doorman who was looking at me in a new light. I had forgotten to give her my condolences.

"Something for Madame Arafat? You can always leave it for her at the desk."

I nodded and patted my brief case as if it contained a missive for the hotel's most famous guest, and returned to the spacious lobby that glowed beneath the Baccarat chandeliers. Though I knew the hotel well, it still managed to bowl me over. With marble halls, unique garden restaurant, wonderful rooftop pool and generous rooms with double showers, this was one of only a handful of *palace hôtels* in Paris, and it had been the perfect choice for a weekend of *amour*.

Bypassing the reception desk, I walked straight through to the Marie Antoinette Salon, which doubled as the bar. The American CEO was already sitting on a sofa by a low table. We had met earlier in the week, in our Paris office, but today he had insisted on neutral ground. His New York firm was about to start trading in Europe and he had been looking for premises nearby. There are many reasons why Paris is not the best place to have a European headquarters, but you can't tell Americans that; they're still in love with the place. I was here now to show him how to deal with a few aggravating EU regulations and he wanted to ensure our conversation was not overheard. Taking off his glasses, he stood up to shake my hand. Though a New Yorker, he was sun-tanned and lean, a few inches taller than me and a few years older. His manicured hands were as smooth as mine.

"I just had the pleasure of sharing the elevator with Mrs Arafat and her henchmen," he said as he sat down. "I hear she has a whole floor here. Must cost her $20,000 a month. But I suppose that's only twenty percent of the $100,000 allowance she got out of Arafat. Now he's gone, I guess she's getting her hands on as much as she can of his $11 billion fortune."

A waiter arrived with the silver teapot of Earl Grey and a tray of teacakes, which the CEO had already ordered for both of us. He was as certain of what I would like as he was about how much money the Palestinian leader left behind, yet I don't suppose anybody outside the Palestinian Authority had any idea of the real amount. Yasser Arafat had died at the age of seventy-five in the Percy Military Hospital more than a month earlier, after being flown to Paris from Ramallah. From her suite in Le Bristol his wife had organised everything, but during those two weeks that he lay dying no Press report seemed capable of mentioning Suha Douad Arafat without using such phrases as "bottle blonde" or "lavish lifestyle". One said: "*The spoiled socialite makes Marie Antoinette seem like a piker.*" Not only did she have a suite at Le Bristol, which she had occupied since leaving Palestine and settling in Paris with her five-year-old daughter in 2000, but she also had a "luxury Paris apartment" and a French country home. Nobody liked the idea of Palestine's First Lady being rich.

"Some of that money was raised for the welfare of the Palestinian people." The CEO opened the silver teapot and gave it a practised stir. "It wasn't for spending on shoes — even Arafat called his wife the new Imelda Marcos."

"I suppose it was better that money was spent on Blahniks than on bombs." I hadn't noticed her shoes.

"It's hardly surprising," he went on, "that the French financial authorities have decided to investigate. I bet the bitch is a real gold digger."

The more the American went on about Mrs Arafat, the more I began to view the widow as the underdog. There was plenty of evidence to show that she was capable of looking after herself, of course, but the same could have been said for both Emma Hamilton and the Countess of Lichtenau, who were disgracefully dealt with when their lovers died. In fact their very obvious ability to look after themselves only seemed to antagonise the world. Like witches, they were damned whatever they did.

"Maybe she'll turn out to have a heart of gold," I said as I opened my briefcase and took out the papers I had brought to show him.

He laughed without humour. "Maybe pigs will fly."

The meeting lasted a little over an hour and afterwards I was glad to get away. I had imagined that the hotel would bring memories of Sophie flooding back, but it seemed impersonal now. My story was just one of many absorbed into the fabric, the Gobbelin tapestries and Savonnerie carpets, which the decades had woven with tales of people such as Suha Arafat, whose lives were far more interesting than mine.

The hotel had the last glimpse of Josephine Baker celebrating fifty years of performance in a gala here just before she died. It saw the coffin of Amschel Rothshild brought down from his room in 1996 after a chambermaid had discovered he had hanged himself using a bath robe chord; aged forty-one, the chairman of Rothschild Asset Management had been due to take over the English arm of the dynasty. And it witnessed a protesting Robert de Niro being led away by half a dozen policemen who had arrested him in his room and hauled him off for nine hours of questioning after his name had been linked to an international prostitution ring. Infuriated, de Niro told *Le Monde* that he would return his Légion d'Honneur and never set foot in the country again, a threat he later retracted.

One resident who never set foot in England again was P. G. Wodehouse. Caught up in the German invasion, he and his wife Ethel were arrested in their villa in Le Touquet in May 1940, and interned in Upper Silesia until the following year when he was nearing the age of sixty and under German law was eligible for release. The couple were moved to Hotel Adlon in Unter der Linden (now the Kempinski Adlon) in Berlin where he made five inoffensive, if unwise wartime broadcasts at the request of CBS, because many of his American fans had been petitioning the German authorities for news of his whereabouts. Entitling the talks "How to be an Internee without Previous Experience", they were designed, he later wrote "to give American readers a humorous description of my adventures". America had not yet entered the war, and the Luftwaffe's bombing blitz of Britain had just begun. The German authorities then broadcast these tapes to Britain and as a result Wodehouse was vilified. In 1943 "Plum" and Ethel, with their Pekingese called Wonder, were moved to

Paris and Le Bristol Hotel. To secure their daily bread and pay hotel bills, Wodehouse could access money owing to him for royalties and other payments around the world only if it was channelled through German banks. This convinced MI5 that he must have been in the pay of the Nazis and he would not be welcome back in Britain again.

A fellow resident at Le Bristol during those war years was John Amery, who tried to recruit Wodehouse for real Nazi propaganda work. He himself made regular broadcasts for the Nazis and set out, unsuccessfully, to enlist British and Commonwealth POWs in a fighting brigade for Germany. Immediately after the war he pleaded guilty to charges of high treason and treachery and was hanged in Wandsworth prison. The son of Leo Amery, who was half Jewish and Secretary of State for the Colonies in Churchill's wartime cabinet, Amery was a virulent anti-semite, and he would have been astonished to discover that a Jewish architect called Lerman had been hidden in Bristol's Room 106 for the duration of the war, from where he continued to redesign the hotel, turning its Art Deco into a Regency style and doubling the size of the guest rooms. His room number was removed from both the door and the register so that he might not be found.

There is a three-act play somewhere in this war-time tragedy, a black French farce involving the opening and closing of many hotel-room and elevator doors, with Wonder yapping at any drape that twitches. After the liberation, Wodehouse was taken in by the French authorities and interviewed by British intelligence officer Malcolm Muggeridge, while the *Observer*'s man in Paris, George Orwell, rushed over from the Hotel Scribe for an interview, providing a fitting finale for the farce.

After my meeting with the American in Le Bristol's Marie Antoinette Salon, I took a brief window of opportunity to find Christmas gifts for my parents, and for James's two children, to take to them in Spain on Christmas Day. I wished I could have indulged in expensive purchases for Sophie. Instead, I had to settle for a few consumable goods for Mum and Dad and a couple of

French football shirts for the boys, leaving them to decide which of them wanted to be Zidane, and which one Thierry Henry.

I was staying at another Bristol, the Hôtel Bristol République, which I had for some time promised to tick off. It was typical Bristol: old, solid, reliable, content with its three stars. It was no *palace hôtel* like Le Bristol, but it was fine.

The next morning was Christmas Eve, and before going down to breakfast I checked my emails. There was one from James. He and his family had already arrived at my parents' villa in Spain where I was about to join them, flying down the following day. "*Just in case you were wondering what last-minute gift to get me,*" he wrote, "*as you're in Paris, you could buy me a Cartier Tank Américaine with a black band and gold case. Otherwise, just bring the usual..*" The usual was nothing. We had a pact: no presents on either birthday or Christmas. I was looking forward to seeing him. He would be intrigued to know about Suha Arafat at Le Bristol.

Friday was a full working day in our Paris office, some of which was taken up with a discreet discussion with our art expert, Jean-Philippe, about the hypothetical disposal of a couple of Expressionist masterpieces. Around five o'clock I returned to my hotel to wash and change into something warmer and more comfortable. With nothing else to divert me, and no other plans, I was vaguely prodded by James's email in a direction that I had already considered exploring. The starting point was the Hôtel de Ville, the heart of the city, where for a while I was entertained by the skaters on the open-air ice rink. It was too cold to stay long, so I wandered up through the Palais Royale, where Paris's first restaurant had opened in 1785, offering, for the first time, a choice of dishes and individual tables for its customers. Regretfully, Lord Bristol could not have appreciated it. He had been in the city half a dozen years earlier, during the American War of Independence, when he had befriended Benjamin Franklin, America's first Minister in France, to try to find some points of reconciliation between Britain and her colony. The French Revolution had kept him away after that.

Half a century later there were several Bristol hotels in Paris. In fact when Hypollite Jammet opened the sumptuous Le Bristol in Rue du Fauburg St-Honoré in 1925, he had to do battle with two other hotels claiming the name, which had been made famous by a grand Hotel Bristol that had stood between his hotel and the Palais Royal on the corner of Rue St Honoré and Place Vendôme. The Prince of Wales, "Duke of Lancaster", heir to Queen Victoria, was among those who enjoyed the original Hotel Bristol's splendid apartments, which consisted of dining rooms, drawing rooms and up to four bedrooms with bath, plus *pensions* for the servants. "*Perhaps the most comfortable hotel in Paris. Patronised by our Royal Family, the general rendezvous of the British and foreign aristocracy and others to whom expense is no object,*" says Murray's guides to Paris in both its 1882 and 1890 editions.

From the Palais Royale I walked up Rue St Honoré, stopping at the corner of Place Vendôme. This was where the nineteenth-century Bristol had been, and now the site was occupied by the much smaller new Hôtel de Vendôme, I stepped into its warmth. The lobby was not extensive and the woman at the desk directed me to the bar on the first floor, up a fine spiral marble staircase. The room was intimate and masculine, with button-back leather chairs and rich mahogany panelling. A quartet of businessmen sat at a table by a window overlooking the street, and the barman stopped his desultory cleaning duties to come to take my order. To give him something to do, I asked for a dry Martini, then took off my scarf and coat and made myself comfortable on a bar stool.

Although quite early, the evening already had about it a late night air, a time when people had nowhere left to go. The barman was from St-Etienne, the industrial town in the south, and had no family to speak of, so he was happy to work on Christmas Eve, he said. He didn't ask about my arrangements, and I was in no hurry to offer details. Instead I mentioned the Hotel Bristol that once occupied this site and I asked him if he knew the story of the world's biggest blue diamond, which is now in the Smithsonian Museum in Washington.

"*Non, Monsieur*," he said, showing polite interest.

"It was first offered to an American millionairess in a room here in the old Bristol," I said, and as neither of us seemed to have anything better to do, I settled back to tell the tale, gauging my words so that they might last no longer than my cocktail. As he listened, he started polishing the already sparkling glasses.

Evalyn Walsh McLean was the daughter of Thomas Walsh, a millionaire who had made his money after discovering and exploiting the Camp Bird gold mine in Quary, Colorado, and she had married Edward "Ned" Beale McLean, whose almost equally rich father had bought the *Washington Post*. For the benefit of her education, Evalyn had visited Paris where she always spent a generous portion of her father's fortune on clothes and hair-styles. But her real passion was jewellery. In 1908, aged nineteen, Evalyn and Ned honeymooned in Europe and the Middle East with $100,000 spending money each from their families. They ended their three-month jaunt at the Bristol in Paris unable to pay the hotel bill. So she cabled her father and he sent fresh credit and his love. She went straight to the jeweller's, Cartier. And there she treated herself to a wedding present, the Star of the East, a 94.8 carat pear-shaped diamond mounted on a platinum links with a 34 carat emerald and 32-grain pearl. It cost $110,000.

Evalyn's love of jewellery and her ability to spend money makes Suha Arafat seem parsimonious. In 1919, after her doting father died, she and Ned left their first child, Vinson, in the care of her mother for a trip to Europe. In Monte Carlo, after playing at the tables one night, they suddenly decided to drive to Paris in their yellow Fiat roadster. Evalyn's maid was put on the express train with the bulk of their luggage but their chauffeur felt too unwell to make the journey, so Ned told him to sit in the back of the car, which he proceeded to drive at a ferocious pace north to the capital.

Some six hundred miles later, the car drew up outside the Bristol in Place Vendôme, ten minutes before the express train arrived from the Mediterranean. When the hotel doorman stepped out to greet the guests, Evalyn looked around to see why the chauffeur was not helping them from their car. The man's eyes were wide, there was spittle on his jacket and he was half on and half off the back seat.

"*Mon dieu!*" the doorman exclaimed. "*Il a frappé le pipe!*"

Somewhere on the high-speed journey the chauffeur had died of a heart attack.

Nobody was more pleased to hear of the dramatic return of Evalyn to Paris than Pierre Cartier, grandson of the jewellery firm's founder. He had sold her the Star of the East and he knew her likes and dislikes. On her honeymoon she had told him of her visit to the harem of Sultan Mehmet VI in Istanbul, where she had been attracted to some of the occupants' jewellery. Now he had just the thing for her: the Hope Diamond. This unprecedented blue diamond had an adventurous past, and he would enjoy embellishing its story for the sales performance of a lifetime. On their previous encounter Evalyn had declared that things that brought bad luck to other people invariably turned to good luck in her hands. Using this as the core of his strategy, Cartier would say that the diamond had been torn from the throat of a woman in the Sultan's harem, and even that it had been stolen from the forehead of a Hindu shrine, just like Wilkie Collins' Moonstone.

What is true about the stone is that it probably came from the Kollur mine in Golconda in India. It was first mentioned in the 1660s, when it was purchased by a French trader, Jean Baptiste Tavernier, since when it had passed through many hands, including those of the kings of France and England, though it took its name from an English banker, Henry Philip Hope, who acquired it in the mid-nineteenth century

Few people in the world could afford the diamond, but Cartier knew Evalyn Walsh McLean had both the desire and the means to acquire it, so he wrapped it in a small box, sealed it with wax, and walked across the Place Vendôme to their suite in the Hotel Bristol. In the couple's room, he laid the small box on the table and, sitting opposite them, slowly unwrapped it as he spun out a story about the jewel's past, engulfing it with tales of mystery and inventing misfortunes that had befallen its owners.

"As we all stared at that diamond," Evalyn recalled, "Monsieur Cartier began to tell us things he did not vouch for... that Tavernier had stolen the gem from a Hindu idol, and was cursed and torn apart by savage beasts. Since then, the diamond had brought bad luck to anyone who wore or even touched it... Monsieur Cartier was most entertaining."

Cartier was not just entertaining, he was a brilliant salesman, and though he did not make the sale on the spot, he had the diamond re-set to her liking and shortly afterwards took it to Washington where the sale was agreed, for $180,000...

At this point in my story a group of Italians appeared in the bar of the Hôtel de Vendôme, demanding the barman's full attention. They were in good humour and wished everyone a merry Christmas before embarking on a long discussion about what they might drink. My tale was pretty well told, so I drained the Martini, slid off my stool, said good night, put on my scarf and coat and headed back on to the street.

Cartier's main shop is in the Rue de la Paix on the opposite side of Place Vendôme. The square itself is full of jewellers; Christmas lights shone in the plate glass windows of Van Cleef & Arple, Bulgari, Chaumet, Reza, Channel and Dior. CCTV cameras were everywhere and a couple of occupied police cars sat silently against the kerb beside The Ritz.

I imagined Pierre Cartier coming across the square from Rue de la Paix with his hand firmly on the valuable parcel tucked in his pocket. Wearing a silk hat and frock coat, the knife-sharp crease of his trousers pricking his oyster-coloured spats, his shoes skipped lightly on the cobbles and his deep blue eyes sparkled as brightly as his wares while his mind worked over the details of the tales he was about to spin.

Just before I reached Rue de la Paix I saw that Cartier had

another, smaller shop on the square. The mesh grilles were down, and the most sparkling items had been removed from the display cases, but there were still a few baubles left to stare at, among them a couple of watches. A Tank Divan had a price tag of 8,000 euros, and a Tank Français 11,600 euros, but there was no Tank Américaine. I took out my mobile phone to text James, to tell him he would have to settle for the usual.

I was tapping in the keys when a car pulled up to the kerb behind me. Doors slammed and high heels clicked on the pavement. I looked round to see a pair of expensive black boots with fur lining. Suha Arafat was with an older woman and two bodyguards, one on a mobile phone, the other scanning the square. I don't know if it was because she had seen me outside Le Bristol and thought I was a resident and therefore a neighbour, or if Pierre Rizk had told her who I was, or perhaps it was just because it was Christmas Eve, but she give me a friendly smile and said hello.

"My brother wanted a watch for Christmas," I explained. "I was just telling him he's out of luck. Are you after something?"

"Perhaps." And then, as if she we re too aware of her reputation as a spendthrift, she added. "For my daughter."

The child's name came to me. "Zahwa? How old is she now?"

"Nine and a half."

I found myself saying that children were a good investment. The warm and worldly face of the older woman, whom I took to be her mother, glowed. Suha came from a Christian family and was educated in a convent, only converting to Islam when she married. I imagined that Zahwa, who was born here in Paris, was looking forward to Christmas like everyone else in town.

There was the sound of locks being undone and we all looked towards the door where lights had come on. Suha and her mother were shopping out of hours, a personal arrangement. As the glass door opened and a pinstriped salesman greeted his clients behind the rising grille, I said good night. Crossing the Rue de la Paix I slipped into the shadows beneath the canopy of another jeweller's.

From there I could see the lights come on in the first floor corner building above Cartier's. Suha Arafat would be looking at jewels for her daughter, and I wished she wouldn't.

I had left the Hôtel de Vendôme before the barman could ask me anything more about the Hope Diamond, which is now one of the most popular exhibits in the Washington museum. If those Italian customers had not arrived in the bar at that moment, the young man from St-Etienne would have asked if the legendary stone had brought Evalyn Walsh McLean bad luck, because that's what everyone wants to know.

Well, I would have told him that her husband, Ned, a lifelong alcoholic, bankrupted the *Washington Post* and died insane in a clinic unable to recognise his own name. Vinson, her oldest and favourite son, died in a car accident just before his tenth birthday, and when she was twenty-five, Evie, Evalyn's only daughter, took an overdose of sleeping pills.

However brilliant the Cartier salesmen were now as they brought out their trinkets to show their wealthy client, whatever stories they spun and however dazzling their wares, I could not help wishing that Zahwa Arafat might not find the diamonds she was hoping for in her stocking on Christmas Day.

20: BEYOND TRAVEL

The Ideal Bristol
The Maghreb
By invitation only

The Ideal Hotel Bristol is an oasis in the desert. Its rooms are washed by air that no one else has breathed. The windows open on to fragrant terraces. There is the sound of water. No one is disturbed. There are clear pools for bathing, into which terrapins sometimes find their way. There is nobody visibly in attendance by the pools. These belong to the guests to enjoy alone. In the palm trees there are colourful parrots that have learned to sing. Hummingbirds feed on hibiscus flowers, bees take nectar for their honey, turtle doves coo. There are hammocks and swings and rocking chairs. Roses flourish year round in occasional beds, aromatic spices fill the vegetable gardens and spill from tubs around the grounds. Guests may pick the flowers.

Rooms are in low white buildings and adobe huts. They are not overlooked. Each has floor cushions, a sofa and a table with a good reading lamp. Notebooks, samplers, pens, playing cards and coloured pencils are provided. Televisions and computers are kept in cupboards. Fridges are fully stocked. There is a music console by the bed. The showers are like Niagara, the bath robes and slippers soft; nightdresses of silk are provided. Though rooms are generally for single occupancy, the beds are queen-size, with down pillows and Egyptian cotton sheets. Roses are left on the pillows every day.

All the guests are women. It is a women-only establishment. Occasionally women book rooms with friends, sometimes with their daughters or mothers. Most come alone.

Some of the staff are male. The maids are female, but

respectful young Arab boys help with the luggage and other handy tasks. There are handsome male masseurs. Everything is done to provide the women with exactly what they desire.

Guests can feel alone, and they can feel truly wanted. There are many devices to improve their comfort. There are baths and treatments, unguents and lotions, massages and therapies. The rooms have ceiling fans as well as air conditioning, and on warm nights guests can ask for Arab boys to go to their rooms with palms to wave. Some of the boys sing, too, and on cold nights can act as bed warmers.

Meals may be taken in the guest's room, on the terraces or by the pools. There are several dining rooms. One has live music where musicians play simple reed flutes and ouds, one has cubicles and damask tablecloths, a third has trestle tables and a cinema screen showing movies without male violence.

A modern hotel is more than an inn or a hostal, even more than a grand palace. It is a destination, a habitat for escape. The Ideal Bristol is a destination beyond travel. It was James who found the location after I had finally come up with the finances, adding a not insubstantial amount of my own after the Munch art deal was done. Many backers were rich women, some of them widows, some famous, others young and successful. Many of them were people I had met on my travels around the Bristol hotels of Europe. All were enthusiastic about the idea.

The Ideal Bristol is an expensive hotel and it is not easy to reach. If guests can afford the journey here, they can afford the rates. But we have also set up a scheme to finance deserving women who cannot afford either the hotel or the cost of the journey. Rooms are allocated to them. They are looked after just as well as the other guests, perhaps better. There are qualified medical people in the hotel, to help heal both mental and physical scars.

In the planning stage I was tempted to name suites after some of our more prominent backers, or after women who could have benefited from respite in a hotel such as this – Emma Hamilton,

Madame Ritz, Dare Wright, Rigoberta Menchú, even Valerie Solanas. But in the end it seemed better not to try to impose another life on those who came to stay. Anonymous room numbers would suffice.

The hotel is the best part of a day's drive to the nearest town, though on clear evenings its distant muezzin manages to drift across the sands at dusk. I live in the hotel. My room is no different from the others, simply furnished with Edvard Munch's *The Madonna* above the bed. Of course they have found the "originals" now, not damaged, like this one is, but in more or less perfect shape. The room is situated between the lobby and the office in a part of the complex where I can come and go without disturbing the guests. I have always enjoyed living in hotels and when I am not occupied with hotel work I expect the staff to treat me like any other guest. On duty, wearing a long collarless coloured cotton shirt like the rest of the employees, I walk round the whole hotel two or three times a day; I try to be attentive to guests but not overbearing, and I always check the reservations. Otherwise I leave everything to the managers.

Even on my days off I usually stay at the hotel. I have become a Sunday writer, researching the history of Frederick Augustus Hervey, 4th Earl of Bristol, and all the hotels that take his name. I trawl the internet, sign up to archives, fire off emails and track down old books that can be sent to me.

My career in finance is over, but my brother James still does good works. Once a month or so he comes here to see how the business is progressing. He is looking for a site to start a second Ideal Bristol, this one in Central America, perhaps in the jungle.

We have not advertised the Maghreb Ideal Bristol and it opened without fanfare. There were no Press announcements, no junkets or other enticements. The fifty rooms would be filled at first by private invitation from our backers, and then by word of mouth. In trying to keep out of the world's glare, we have forbidden photography. Guests are free, however, to make sketches. The first month or two was quiet, and we wondered if we had a disaster on our hands, if we had entirely overestimated the need for the Ideal Bristol. Some weeks it was almost empty. But little by little the news spread and by the fifth month we were obliged to turn some customers away.

In fact, it would be fair to say that all was going exceptionally well until early one midweek evening in September, six months after we had opened. I was at the reception desk, standing in for an employee who had taken a few days off to visit her sick mother, when a call came from one of the guests. The voice was lazy and beguiling, with an attractive French Swiss accent that I recognised at once. A display on the phone told me her name and that she was in the Great Poolside Room 25.

"Madame Arouet?"

"I would like a mint tea brought to my room."

I hesitated. Why was she here? Did she know it was me? Lowering my voice in the hope of disguising it, I said, "Certainly, madam, I'll have a boy bring you one straight away."

"I don't want a boy," she said. "I want you."

Stunned, I put down the phone. Then I clicked on the screen in front of me to call up the hotel register and scroll down to Room 25. Sophie Marie Arouet had an address in Prague. I had thought nothing of it when I had seen the booking, but now I recalled that Arouet was Voltaire's real name. I had come to the desertto forget about the woman who had left me for a dog. Now she had followed me into this wilderness, into my ultimate Bristol, my final place of escape. What could I do? We promised to give our guests all they wanted. The Bristol's reputation was at stake.

Ten minutes later I was knocking on her door with a glass of mint tea on a small copper tray and no idea what to expect, even less idea as to how I should behave.

However well I had known this particular guest, it was a shock to see her after several years. Without makeup and fresh from the shower, she looked lovely. The wrinkles round her eyes were engaging and the few grey hairs that glistened in her auburn mane gave her a maturity that I wanted to embrace, to dive into so that I could return to, and continue to be part of, the story of her life. Yet she gave no indication that she knew who I was and when she said, "Come in", she could have been addressing any member of the staff. I could not tell if this was a game or if she had suffered some kind of breakdown and her memory had been wiped clean. For the moment, I continued to play the part of the hotel waiter, averting my eyes with some difficulty from her silk nightdress, which showed that she was still in excellent shape. The glass doors on to the terrace were open and the warm breeze that ruffled the surface of the pool beyond drifted round its hem. Her washed skin smelled so familiar that my blood rushed to my face.

"Put it on the table," she said.

"Yes, madam."

"Then come to bed."

So Sophie and I were in the sack again. But it was different this time. I was courteous, a little distant, anxious to do her bidding, to give pleasure. At the Bristol, we always aim to please. She called me "boy" and I called her "madam" and never once did we use each other's name or give any hint that we knew anything of the other's past. We slotted back together easily, and we slept in each other's arms.

I left her in the night, stealing barefoot on to the terrace, then slipping into the pool, swimming alone, reflectively, as silently as I could, hoping none of the women guests would see me.

The next morning, torn between wanting to dash out and find Sophie again and thinking that I should hide until she had gone, I remained in my room. Just before midday I could bear it no longer. When two people are thinking of each other there will always be coincidences; they are bound to meet. Sophie arrived in the lobby at exactly the same moment that I did. Her bag was packed. The people carrier was waiting outside. She avoided looking at me and went over to the desk, where she asked to make a reservation for the first weekend of the following month. In fact, she asked to spend the first weekend of every month here for a year. The receptionist glanced across to me for approval for such an unusual arrangement, though Sophie refused to turn round. I nodded.

"Friday to Sunday?" the receptionist asked.

"Yes." Sophie said. "If I want to extend it to Sunday night, too, I will let you know."

"That will be twenty-four nights altogether then."

By now I had hidden myself behind a palm in the lounge, not wanting to make a scene in front of the staff, but I was sure that she knew I was listening. Twenty-four nights, more than three solid weeks, was probably more time than we had spent together in the last year of our relationship, when I was always away. Though I did not want to see her go to whatever life she had in Prague, this was not like our last encounter. I felt no sorrow, just real regret: regret that I was the person I was, and that I would never change.

The transporter's engine started. I had to be sure that she would return. When she reached the vehicle I called out her name and hurried towards her. She stopped, but did not turn to look at me. From behind I took her hand.

"Sophie, please, tell me just one thing." My throat was dry as the desert that was beginning to burn in the morning sun. "What happened to Voltaire?"

She turned towards me then. Her eyes were lustrous with memories of disappointment and puppy love.

"I kept him," she whispered. "I couldn't give him back."

"So you have…"

She nodded. "Two dogs. Barry and Voltaire. You were right. They are a bit of a handful." Trying to laugh, she caught her breath, and it made her shiver. I found her a handkerchief and she blew her nose. "But I do love them."

"They could not have a better home."

"How would you know? I don't suppose you remember what it was like living with me. You were hardly ever there when we were together."

I could not argue with her, so I said, "I hope you like our

hotel. It was designed just…" I was going to say, "just for you," but she interrupted.

"It's no good caring for women in general when you can't look after any one in particular." It was a wistful remark, not an admonishment.

"I'll make sure you have the best room next time you come."

She sighed. There was nothing to be done. Reaching up, she kissed me on the cheek. "*Il faut cultiver notre jardin*," she whispered. Then she climbed aboard the transporter and it started off into the dust of the desert.

The last line of Voltaire's *Candide* lingered in the cloudy haze like a mirage. *We cannot hope to change the world if we don't tend our own gardens.* I thought of Lord Bristol, begetter of hotels, who did as he pleased, roaming around Europe for years on end without any care for either his home or his wife. And I thought: That's why I like hotels, whatever they are called.

They are as far as we can possibly get from our own backyards.

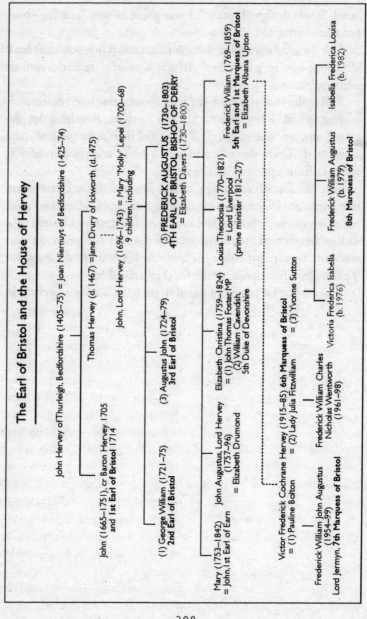

The Earl of Bristol and the House of Hervey

John Hervey of Thurleigh, Bedfordshire (1405–75) = Joan Niernuyt of Bedfordshire (1425–74)

Thomas Hervey (d. 1467) = Jane Drury of Ickworth (d. 1475)

John, Lord Hervey (1696–1743) = Mary "Molly" Lepel (1700–68) 9 children, including

John (1665–1751), cr Baron Hervey 1705 and **1st Earl of Bristol** 1714

(5) FREDERICK AUGUSTUS (1730–1803) 4TH EARL OF BRISTOL, BISHOP OF DERRY = Elizabeth Davers (1730–1800)

(3) Augustus John (1724–79) 3rd Earl of Bristol

Frederick William (1769–1859) **5th Earl and 1st Marquess of Bristol** = Elizabeth Albana Upton

Louisa Theodosia (1770–1821) = Lord Liverpool (prime minister 1812–27)

Elizabeth Christina (1759–1824) = (1) John Thomas Foster, MP (2) William Cavendish, 5th Duke of Devonshire

(1) George William (1721–75) 2nd Earl of Bristol

John Augustus, Lord Hervey (1757–96) = Elizabeth Drummond

Mary (1753–1842) = John, 1st Earl of Earn

Frederick William Augustus (b. 1979) **8th Marquess of Bristol**

Isabella Frederica Louisa (b. 1982)

Victoria Frederica Isabella (b. 1976)

Victor Frederick Cochrane Hervey (1915–85) **6th Marquess of Bristol** = (1) Pauline Bolton   = (2) Lady Julia Fitzwilliam   = (3) Yvonne Sutton

Frederick William Charles Nicholas Wentworth (1961–98)

Frederick William John Augustus (1954–99) **Lord Jermyn, 7th Marquess of Bristol**